COLLINS REAL-WORLD TECHNOLOGY

Series editors:

Colin Chapman
Regional Adviser,
The Engineering Council,
Technology Enhancement Programme

Mike Finney
Head of Technology,
William Farr CofE Comprehensive School, Welton

COMMUNICATING DESIGN

The Authors

Mike Finney has been involved in the development and teaching of
Design & Technology for 20 years. He has previously co-authored: *Collins*
CDT: Foundation Course, and *Design and Communication*; *Collins*
Technology for Key Stage 3: The Process, Techniques and Resources, and
What's IT all About?

Val Charles, formerly an Advisory Teacher for Business Education and for
Design & Technology, has co-authored: *Collins Technology for*
Key Stage 3: The Process, Techniques and Resources, and
What's IT all About?

COMMUNICATING DESIGN

Mike Finney
Head of Technology,
William Farr CofE Comprehensive School, Welton

Val Charles
National Curriculum Assessment Co-ordinator

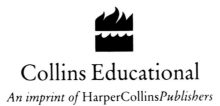

Collins Educational
An imprint of HarperCollinsPublishers

Contents

4·Drawings to work from   TECHNICAL DRAWING

5·Real-World Design   CASE STUDIES

Published in 1995 by Collins Educational

An imprint of HarperCollins*Publishers*

77-85 Fulham Palace Road
Hammersmith
London
W6 8JB

©1995 Collins Educational

Mike Finney and Val Charles assert the moral right to be identified as the authors of this work.

ISBN 0 00 327350 4

Designed by Ken Vail Graphic Design (production management: Chris Williams)

Cover photographs by Peter Sharp and Imagelink

Illustrated by Peter Dennis, Julie Free, Keith Howard, Mike Lacey, Jake Tebbit and Alan Vincent

Location and studio photography by Peter Sharp

Printed and bound by HarperCollins Hong Kong

Commissioning Editor: Graham Bradbury

Project Editor: Alison Walters

Production: Angela Davies

What's this book about?

This book is about communicating design. It shows you how to use graphic media and techniques to communicate stages within your Design & Technology projects – from your initial ideas to the final design proposals. From freehand sketching, modelling and presentation drawing through to working drawings, this book will support all your designing and making activities.

For each stage of the designing process, you will find hints and tips on how to make effective drawings and models to record, develop and communicate your ideas, produce detailed working drawings and accurately plan the production of your chosen design.

You do not need to be an artist to be able to communicate your design ideas. This book shows you how you can develop your skills to produce quality design work.

To show you how the D&T skills you are learning in school relate to design and technology in the real world, each chapter includes case studies taken from business and industry, which show you how the graphic techniques detailed in the book are used in the designing and making of real products by industrial and commercial designers and manufacturers.

The case studies illustrate the design process in many aspects of design and technology – examples range from garment design to engineering design.

Throughout the book, you will find activities and exercises to help you practise and develop your graphic, modelling and designing skills.

You can use this book as a reference at each stage of your Design & Technology work, or to develop your own skills at your own pace.

1·Getting started

Michael Gibbs, at Griffen Paper Mill in the southwest of England, is one of the few people left in Britain who manufacture paper by hand. The market for handmade paper is very specialised, and Griffen Paper Mill has identified a 'market niche' in the repair of ancient books and documents. Bookbinders and the British Library are amongst the mill's customers – and one of its recent tasks was making paper for repairing pages in a very old book for Canterbury Cathedral.

The process that Michael follows is similar to that used up until the end of the eighteenth century. The mill buys in waste textile fibres and Michael beats them into paper pulp using a 'Hollander' beater (a machine which was invented during the seventeenth century). These fibres are transferred to a vat and mixed with water to form the paper pulp. Then a paper mould (a fine wire mesh on a wooden frame) is dipped into the vat. When the mould is lifted out, a layer of pulp has collected on the top, which, once the water has drained from it, forms the sheet of paper.

CHOOSING MATERIALS

The materials and equipment that you choose to work with when you are designing will depend very much on what you want to do and how far ahead you are with your design. Different materials and equipment are needed at each stage of your work. For instance, when you first start forming ideas you will want to work with materials that will allow you to work quickly, whereas at the working-drawing stage you will need to use materials which enable you to be very precise and show exactly how you intend to realise your design.

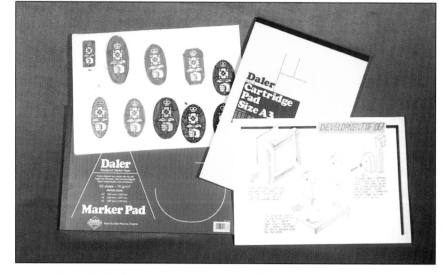

Fig. 1.2 *It is important to choose the right support for the job.*

Get the right support

Drawing surfaces such as paper and card are sometimes called 'supports'. It is very important to use the correct support for the type of drawing you are doing and for the medium that you have chosen to work with. Soft pencils work best on a rough surface; inks and markers require a paper or board which will not allow them to run or bleed; and wet media such as gouache and watercolours need a specially prepared surface which will not wrinkle when water is applied.

Papers and boards

There is an enormous selection of papers and boards available, ranging from newsprint (paper for newspapers) and layout paper to high-quality illustration board and expensive heavy watercolour paper.

Paper is described by its size, weight and texture. You have probably noticed the letters A3 or A4 on sketchbooks or notepads.

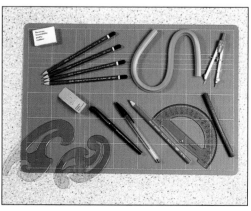

Fig. 1.1 *Choose the right tools for the job.*

The newly formed sheets are then 'couched' (laid down) between layers of felt and pressed to remove any remaining water. After pressing, the sheets and felts are separated and the paper is dried.

Of course, this is not an ideal method for producing paper in the quantity that we use it today! Now there are machines that use much the same process, but produce paper automatically and on a much larger scale. (The first practical paper-making machines were introduced around 1800, and machines in use today use the same principles.)

There are two main types of paper-making machine:

1 Cylinder mould machines, which are used to produce high-quality watercolour papers like the ones you use in school.

2 Foudrinier machines (like the one shown here), which are faster than cylinder mould machines but cannot produce such high-quality paper. Most mass-produced paper (like the paper for this book) is produced on this type of machine.

These letters and numbers refer to the international standard paper sizing system, in which an A0 sheet of paper has an area of 1 square metre. A sheet of A1 paper (594 × 841 mm) is half the size of an A0 sheet. The next size down is A2 which is exactly half the size of A1. A3 is half the size of A2, and so on, down to A6. The diagram in Figure 1.3 will help you to understand the sizing system. You will probably find that A3 paper is the most convenient size for most of your work.

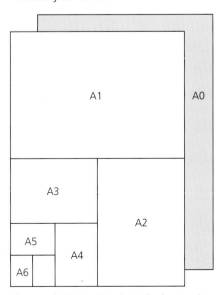

Fig. 1.3 *The international standard paper sizes*

Watch your weight

The thickness and density of a sheet of paper is usually described by its *weight*. For example, the paper used in a photocopier normally has a weight of about 80 gsm. The letters 'gsm' stand for 'grammes per square metre'. Ordinary watercolour paper has a weight of 300 gsm. In other words, an A0 size sheet of this paper actually weighs 300 grammes, and a single A2 sheet weighs 75 grammes. If you compare the thickness of the two types of paper you will see that a sheet of watercolour paper is much thicker than a sheet of copier paper. The thicker the paper the more it weighs. The pages of this book are made from 105 gsm paper. The size of each page is A4. What do you think the weight of each page is?

The rough and the smooth

It is also very important to consider the texture of the paper that you use in your design work. The roughness of the paper surface is known as the 'tooth',

and it is determined by the way the paper is made. There are three types of paper surfaces available: hot pressed (HP), cold pressed (CP) and rough. Hot-pressed paper has a smooth surface with very little tooth, making it ideal for use with pencils, pens, ink and washes. Cold-pressed paper has a rougher surface and is suitable for drawing with chalk, soft-leaded pencils and gouache. Rough paper has a textured surface which is very good for working in watercolour and for work where paint, ink and pencil are mixed. Good quality papers can be really expensive, but a high-standard cartridge paper with a weight of about 120 gsm will be suitable for most of your work.

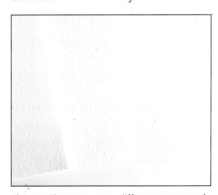

Fig. 1.4 *There are many different textures of paper available.*

Quality control at Berol Ltd

Berol Ltd, based in King's Lynn, is a company which manufactures and distributes writing instruments and artists' materials. Its products are exported to at least 98 countries, even Japan, where some of Berol's major competitors are based.

Although we do not know when the first pencil was invented, Conrad Gesner, a Swiss naturalist, described his 'writing rod held in a wooden case' in his book Treatise on Fossils, *published in 1565. There have been a number of variations since that time. Today, the pencil industry is an international business, using raw materials from every corner of the globe.*

The pencil 'leads' are made of a mixture of graphite (a natural mineral similar to coal) and clay, finely ground, thoroughly mixed, and fired in ovens to produce a strong fused stick, similar to chinaware. Berol use amorphous graphite from Mexico in the manufacture of their pencils. Berol's invention, the 'attrition mill', blows two jets of highly compressed air, containing graphite particles, directly at each other, enabling the particles of graphite to grind themselves into powder.

The clay, which comes mainly from Bavaria, is mixed with water and refined to remove all grit and heavier elements, leaving only the finest microscopic particles to be mixed with the graphite.

MAKING YOUR MARK

Charcoal

Fig. 1.5 *Charcoal comes in a wide range of pencils and sticks*

Charcoal is made out of wood (usually willow or vine twigs) which has been deliberately and carefully burnt. It has been used as a drawing material for centuries. You can buy charcoal today in either stick form or pencil form. It is very effective for communicating design because it allows you to work quickly to show the general outlines of your ideas. It is ideal for sketching on a large scale and is an excellent material for shading. You will not be able to show the fine details of your design with charcoal, but it is excellent for giving general impressions.

When you use charcoal you should take care, as it smudges very easily. However, this can at times be used to advantage, and charcoal work is often deliberately smudged to create tonal effects. To prevent your finished charcoal drawings smudging and making a mess of your folder, they need to be fixed. This involves spraying the drawing with a fixative spray which seals the surface of the work so that it cannot be accidentally smudged. Take care when using fixative sprays. Always use them in a well-ventilated area or a special spray booth.

Pencils

Pencils are the most commonly used drawing instrument and they are available in a wide variety of types and styles. You can buy up to 19 different grades of traditional graphite pencils. They are graded according to their degree of hardness. The letter H is used to indicate the harder pencils and B is used to denote the softer ones. Soft pencils produce a black line while

the harder types produce a grey one. The softest grade, 8B, is used mainly by artists, while the hardest grade, 9H, is often used by stonemasons.

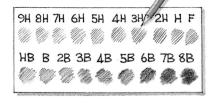

Fig. 1.6 *The range of graphite pencil grades*

Clutch and fine-lead pencils

Many people prefer to use clutch pencils and fine-lead pencils. These have plastic barrels, rather like ball pens, with a push-button mechanism which feeds the lead out of the tip, ready for drawing. Clutch pencils have their own sharpener built into the pencil, whereas fine-lead pencils have leads which are so fine that they never need sharpening. Both types of pencil use graphite and polymer leads which, like traditional graphite pencils, are available in varying degrees of hardness.

The graphite and clay are then mixed together in varying proportions. It is these proportions that determine the degree of hardness of the pencil. The more graphite that is used in the mixture, the softer and blacker the pencil will be.

The casing for the 'lead' is made from Californian cedar wood. The wood is first sawn into slats, each six or seven pencils wide. It is then seasoned, and run through a grooving machine. The grooves are impregnated with a resinous binding material that locks the wood fibres and stops them splitting. The graphite/clay sticks are then laid in the grooves. Glue is applied to a second slat, which is similarly grooved, and the two slats are pressed together to form a sandwich. These 'sandwiches' are washed, thoroughly dried, and fed into a moulding machine which forms them into individual pencils. Following the application of several coats of lacquer they are hot-foil stamped with the brand name and grade before they are sharpened.

Every pencil is rigorously inspected. Laboratory staff sample and check their quality to ensure a perfect finished product, both in appearance and performance.

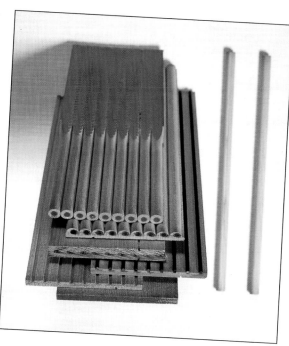

A pencil is born: slats, sandwiches and individual pencils

Making your point

Keeping a sharp point on your pencil is very important, especially if your drawings have to be accurate and show precise details. Most pencils can be sharpened using a bench-mounted rotary machine or a small pocket-sized sharpener. Soft pencils are best sharpened with a sharp knife blade, as the points can break in conventional sharpeners.

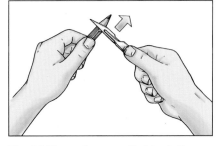

Fig. 1.8 *Sharpening a pencil with a knife*

Always take care when using knives – hold the pencil firmly in one hand and cut away from your body. Cut with a slicing action and rotate the pencil after each cut in order to make an even point. After sharpening a pencil with a knife, it is a good idea to use a piece of glass paper to make a really sharp point.

Ball pens

Ball pens are very useful for making quick sketches and recording ideas as they come to you. They were originally thought of in the late 1890s but the product was not patented until 1937. Since then they have been developed into versatile and inexpensive writing instruments.

They require very little care and maintenance and will successfully make marks on a wide range of papers and boards. The ball pen is so-called because its tip consists of a ball housed in a socket. The ball transfers a special quick-drying ink from an inner plastic tube on to the paper. There is vast range of ball pens available in a variety of ink colours and in several different line widths. They can be used for line work, texture and shading.

Fig. 1.9 *You can buy a range of ball pens in the shops.*

The use of other drawing instruments, such as coloured pencils and felt-tip pens will be explored in the next chapter.

Fig. 1.7 *Clutch and fine-lead pencils*

John Greed trained as a product designer (he has a BA in Industrial Design Engineering), and is now one of Europe's leading 'organic' designers – basing his designs for everyday items on living things, especially sea animals.

He set up his own workshop so that he could experiment with a variety of animal forms using a wide range of materials – wood, polyester resins, GRP, carbon fibre and advanced composites. The strength and lightness of such materials make possible the production of new and unusual shapes. This is something that John is exploring for the household market (his aim being to introduce good organic design into the domestic environment) as well as for the art market.

FREEHAND SKETCHING

The most suitable form of drawing for generating and recording ideas is freehand sketching. As the name suggests, this type of drawing is done without the help of drawing aids such as a ruler or a pair of compasses. You need to record your ideas as quickly as possible before you forget them – using a ruler would slow down this process and break up the flow of ideas. Good freehand sketches are lively and interesting, and provide a record of your thinking process. Sketches drawn with a ruler look dull and lifeless.

Ideas can be explained in a sketch more easily than in words. Sketches are very effective in communicating your ideas to other people, but more important at this stage in the design process, they enable you to see your own ideas more clearly and help you to go on and develop them.

Freehand sketches can be made using any medium that allows you to work quickly. Pencil, fineline marker pen, charcoal and ball pen are all suitable. You should use whatever equipment you are most comfortable with. Sketches can be made on a wide variety of surfaces. Some people prefer to work in sketchbooks on cartridge paper, but many designers work on layout paper which allows

Fig. 1.10 *A student's freehand fashion sketch in pencil and ball pen*

them to overlay it and trace through if they need to redraw or develop an idea. However, you may have a moment of inspiration when cartridge paper or layout paper will not be to hand. The important thing is that you get your idea down in some way, so if this happens you can always find an old envelope or piece of scrap paper to make a rough drawing! Do remember to keep all your drawings, even the rough sketches.

Design is about communicating. To be able to draw well and communicate fluently using graphic media takes time so don't worry if your drawings don't look like John's to begin with. Remember that everyone can draw – it just takes a little practice to be good at it!

Getting some exercise

The following exercises are intended to help you develop your freehand sketching skills. Try working through them.

1 Begin by holding your pen or pencil lightly between your thumb and first finger. Hold your hand so that it can move easily across the paper, freely in all directions. Don't plant your hand on the paper and draw by moving your fingers – move your whole hand.

Fig. 1.11 *Holding a pencil correctly will help you sketch more easily.*

2 Once you have got the feel of the pen or pencil and have made a few marks on the paper, try drawing lines. Start by drawing diagonal lines like the ones in Figure 1.12. Diagonal lines are the easiest to draw naturally – try drawing both ways and see which you find easier. Can you think why it is easier to draw diagonal lines in one direction than the other? Let your hand move freely across the page. Draw quickly, and don't worry if the lines are not straight – it doesn't matter at this stage.

John's work is inspired by the shapes of dolphins and flying mantas, like the 'Mocean' chair shown on the right (a name that implies both the sea [ocean] and movement [motion]).

*The 'Eden' mirror, also shown on the right, is based on folded fabric and hand cast in a variety of composite materials. John uses graphics throughout the process of designing and making his products – from getting his initial ideas down on paper to working drawings. In the early stages of his work, John uses **freehand sketching** to help him to generate and explore his ideas.*

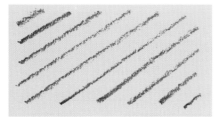

Fig. 1.12

3 Now try drawing horizontal lines. Draw the lines approximately 75mm long, keeping them as straight as possible (without using a ruler). Remember to draw by moving your arm across the paper, using your little finger as a support if necessary. Try doing the same thing with vertical lines. (Don't cheat by turning the paper around!)

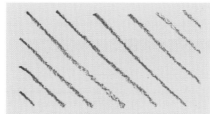

Fig. 1.14

4 To develop your pencil control further, draw two dots about 100mm apart and then join them with your pencil, as shown in Figure 1.14. Repeat this exercise at least 10 times and then try the same thing with vertical lines.

Like an athlete, it is a good idea to 'warm up' before you start. These exercises can be used as part of a warm-up routine before you begin drawing. Remember that to be good at drawing takes practice. Try to spend a few minutes drawing every day – you will be surprised how quickly your confidence will grow and your work improve.

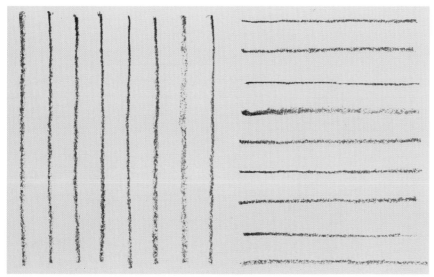

Fig. 1.13 *Horizontal and vertical lines, drawn freehand*

Useful tip

When drawing lines, hold the pencil at an angle so that you can see the point. This will enable you to control the pencil much more accurately.

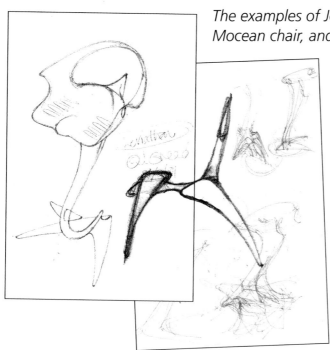

The examples of John's sketches shown here are those for the Mocean chair, and a progression of drawings for a bar stool.

The freehand sketches are made with a ball pen or large soft pencil on cartridge paper or in a small sketch book. As the work progresses, John gradually develops his sketches to full size using either layout paper or tracing paper. Working at full size allows him to fully explore the scale and form of his designs.

In order to be a successful designer in business terms, John feels that the ability to sell is more important than the ability to design, and that the crossover from artistic skills to marketing skills is a difficult transition to make – designing can be quite an introvert process, whereas marketing and promoting one's

DEVELOPING YOUR FREEHAND SKETCHING

So far, the practice exercises in this chapter have been designed to help you get used to holding a pencil correctly and to increase your self confidence in using one. The suggestions for practice on these pages will help you to develop your skills further and enable you to sketch circles and curves by showing you how to construct simple frames or guidelines within which to draw. The camera in Figure 1.15 has been drawn in this way. Remember to keep your pencil sharp, and aim to draw as freely and as quickly as possible. Avoid the temptation to use a ruler or straight edge – you must learn to control the pencil yourself.

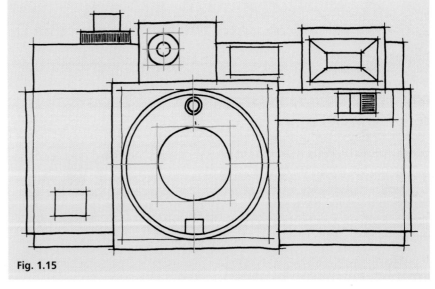

Fig. 1.15

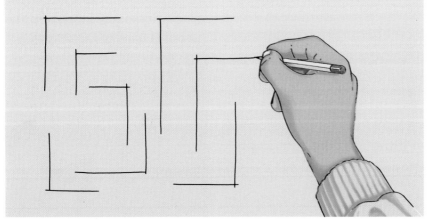

Fig. 1.16 *Drawing right angles*

Fig. 1.17 *Drawing squares and rectangles*

products requires an outgoing, and to some extent extrovert skill. If a person is a bad designer but good at marketing, they will still sell something, while a talented designer, with no selling ability or back-up, would find survival in the commercial world extremely difficult.

From an early stage, John was very much aware that wastage of materials and workshop inefficiencies could cost him a lot of money, and he decided that he would concentrate on doing things which made the best economic sense. He carefully evaluated his production processes – developing plans, making prototypes in MDF (medium-density fibreboard), covering them in glass fibre, polishing, making moulds, applying carbon fibre – determined to get it right economically! His proposals always include a preliminary costing, like the one shown here. Based on these figures, the estimated selling price is £160.00 + VAT. This, however, does not take into consideration the moulding and pattern costs. A percentage of these development costs would need to be added to the costings to make them accurate.

Carbon fibre stool – Cost estimation

Materials:

0.6 sq.m. carbon fibre @ £15.00 per sq.m.	=	£9.00
2.5 sq.m. glass roving @ £4.00 per sq.m.	=	£10.00
0.7 kg epoxy resin @ £8.00 per kg	=	£5.60
Total materials	**=**	**£24.60**

Labour:

Cutting the material	= 10 mins
Release agents	= 5 mins
Gel and lay up	= 20 mins
Cutting and sanding	= 15 mins
Finishing and spraying	= 10 mins
Assembly	= 2 mins
Packing and extra	= 10 mins

Total labour (1.2 hrs @ £22.00 per hour)	=	£26.40
Postage and packing and insurance	=	£5.00
Total costs (£56 rounded up)	=	£60.00
My profit (30%)	=	£20.00
Retail profit (100%)	=	£80.00
Total selling price (excluding VAT)	=	£160.00

Getting some exercise

1 Once you are confident drawing horizontal and vertical lines, try the exercise shown in Figure 1.16. It consists of drawing right angles. Begin by drawing a vertical line and then draw a horizontal line at one of the ends of the vertical line, at right angles to it. Draw quickly and keep your hand moving, supported by your little finger if necessary.

2 After you have practised drawing right angles, try joining them together to form squares and rectangles (Fig. 1.17).

This is a very valuable exercise because most objects that you are likely to want to draw can be simplified and drawn as basic geometric shapes; and, drawn lightly, these squares and rectangles can be used as frames for drawing other shapes. The next exercise (Fig. 1.18) shows how circles and ellipses can be constructed within a simple square or rectangular framework.

3 Circles and ellipses can be easily sketched freehand if you draw a simple frame to guide you. To draw a circle, begin by lightly drawing a freehand square the same width as the required diameter of the circle.

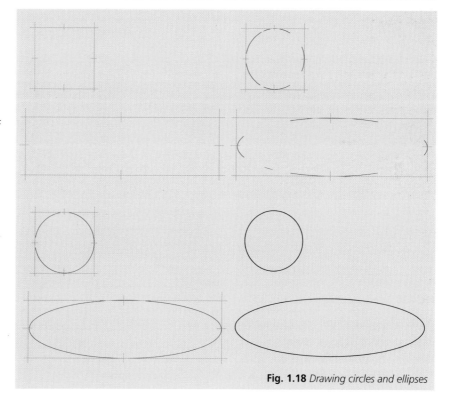

Fig. 1.18 *Drawing circles and ellipses*

Find the approximate centre of each side and mark it with a short line, as shown in Figure 1.18. This is the point where the circle will touch the square.

An ellipse is constructed in a similar way, except that a rectangle, rather than a square, is drawn as the frame. Again, mark the points where the ellipse will touch the sides of the rectangle.

Begin drawing in the shape of the circle or ellipse by sketching a small arc at each point where the shape touches the frame. Gradually extend the arcs until they meet each other to form the outline shape. Sketch the shape very lightly, and then, when you are happy with it, make the outline stronger by pressing more firmly or going over it with a softer pencil.

3-DIMENSIONAL DRAWING

Most of the drawing that you have done so far has been 2-dimensional (i.e. it has represented height and width to show one view or side of an object). In reality, most objects have not only an outline shape, they also have a solid form. So, when drawing objects to make them look realistic, you need to be able to represent their depth as well as their height and width to show all 3 dimensions.

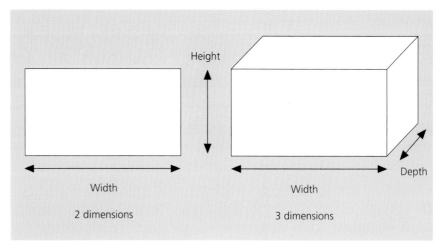

Fig. 1.19 *Drawing in 2 and 3 dimensions*

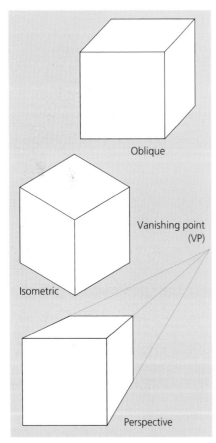

Fig. 1.20 *Types of 3-dimensional drawing*

There are several methods of creating 3-dimensional pictorial drawings. They can be drawn freehand or with the help of drawing instruments. At this stage try drawing freehand – this will help you to develop your sketching skills.

Figure 1.20 shows some of the techniques used to draw simple 3-dimensional sketches – oblique, isometric and perspective. As you can see, each drawing shows three sides of the object, and so conveys more information than 2-dimensional drawings.

Oblique

The oblique technique is the easiest method of 3-dimensional drawing. Begin by drawing the front view as normal and then add the top and sides by drawing lines at 45° from it.

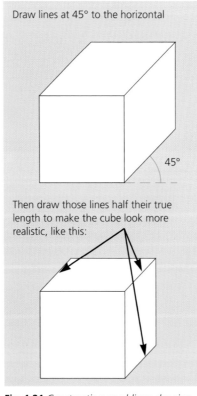

Fig. 1.21 *Constructing an oblique drawing*

Oblique drawing gives an accurate view of the front of the object, but distorts the view of the sides and the top. When making measured oblique drawings you will find that the top and sides appear out of proportion if you draw them to their true length. To overcome this the 45° lines are drawn at half their true length (Fig. 1.21).

Isometric

In isometric drawings the horizontal lines of the object are drawn at an angle of 30°, as shown in Figure 1.22. Like the oblique drawing, it shows three sides but here they *all* appear slightly distorted. Drawing isometric views requires more practice than the oblique technique, but the results do tend to look more realistic.

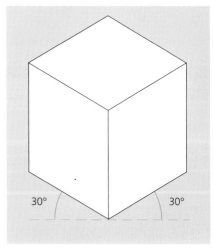

Fig. 1.22

Perspective

The most realistic 3-dimensional drawings are made using perspective-drawing techniques. There are several ways of making perspective drawings using a number of different 'vanishing points' (these are explained later in this chapter). For the time being, when sketching cubes, make all the horizontal lines converge at one vanishing point (single-point perspective) as shown in the perspective drawing in Figure 1.20.

Crating

So far, your drawing has mostly consisted of straight lines, boxes and cubes, which are important in helping you to construct more detailed drawings. Most objects are easier to draw if you begin by drawing them as simple, basic geometric shapes and forms, and then add the detail later (Fig. 1.23).

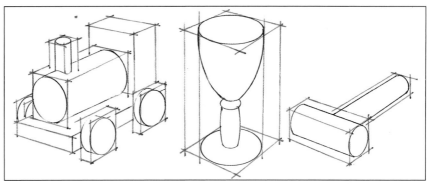

Fig. 1.23

The technique of drawing a box within which to construct your drawing is known as 'crating'. Imagine an object fitted tightly into a box or crate. It is such a good fit that it does not rattle or move about – in fact it touches the crate at several points. Figure 1.24 shows a cylinder which has been drawn by first constructing a crate and then sketching the cylinder within it.

All curves, circles and ellipses can be drawn using this technique. Draw the crate first, mark the points where the object will touch it and then draw in the shape.

Any 3-dimensional drawing method can be used to draw crates – oblique, isometric or perspective.

Proportion

To make your drawing look realistic, you must try to make sure that it is in proportion. Proportion is the relationship between the height, width and depth of an object.

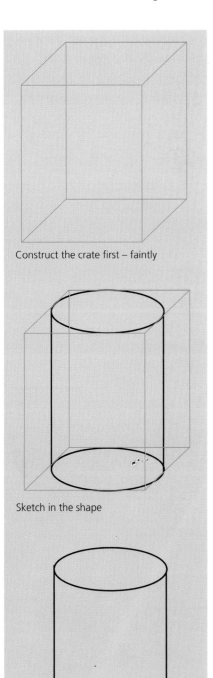

Construct the crate first – faintly

Sketch in the shape

Rub out the crate

Fig. 1.24 *Crating*

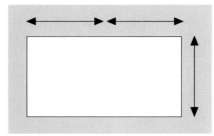

Fig. 1.25

Sometimes you see artists with one eye closed, holding out a pencil at arm's length. They do this to measure the proportion of the things that they are drawing. The rectangle shown in Figure 1.25 is twice as wide as it is high – it has a proportion of 2:1.

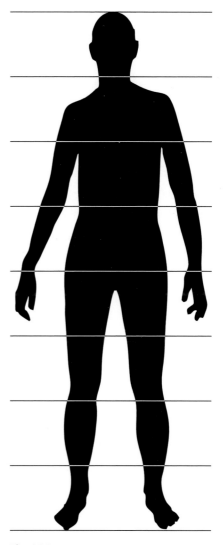

Fig. 1.26

The proportion of the human figure can be divided according to the size of the head. (The total height of an adult is usually eight times the length of their head – a proportion of 8:1.)

Useful tip

Construct your drawing with a 2H pencil and then draw in the outline and details with an HB.

Richard Costall and Ken Allen (who is pictured on the left) have both had wide experience in the construction industry, and their staff include architects, building surveyors, senior and junior technicians, designers and chartered town planners. Together they form Costall Allen Design, architects and design consultants based in Lincoln.

The first stage of any project consists of the prospective client supplying an initial brief outlining the purpose of the building, size, site information, budget available, etc. From this, Costall Allen Design produce provisional line drawings. If the client is happy with these, a more detailed brief is written which enables Costall Allen Design to come up with design schemes in colour and in perspective to illustrate to their customers what the project will look like.

PERSPECTIVE DRAWING

The most realistic way of representing large 3-dimensional design ideas is through perspective drawing. Unlike the forms of 3-dimensional drawing described so far, perspective drawing gives the impression of depth and distance by taking into account the fact that horizontal lines appear to converge at some imaginary point in the distance.

You can see this by looking at buildings, straight roads or railway lines.

Fig. 1.27

We naturally see things in perspective, so drawings done in this way can appear very lifelike (Fig. 1.27).

Fig. 1.28

*Costall Allen Design have used **single-point perspective** to produce this drawing of the north elevation of the Hartpury College in Gloucestershire. As you can see, trees and other foreground details have been sketched in to give depth.*

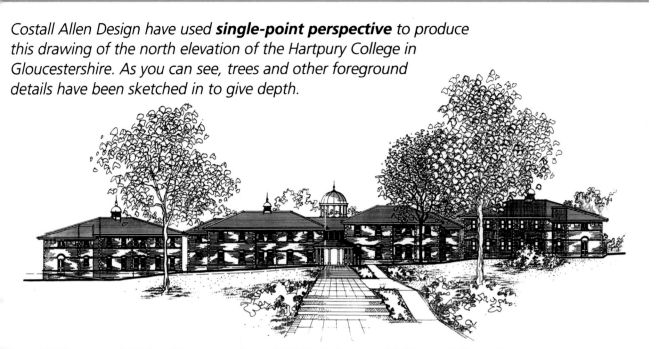

Single-point perspective

The single-point perspective technique shows objects 'flat on', rather like oblique drawing. Lines are taken from each corner to a single common vanishing point. The dice shown in Figure 1.29 has been drawn using this method. The position of the vanishing point is important. If it is placed too close to the object the drawing will be too distorted.

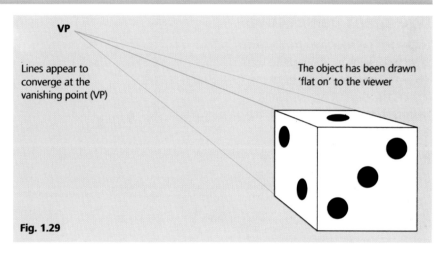

VP

Lines appear to converge at the vanishing point (VP)

The object has been drawn 'flat on' to the viewer

Fig. 1.29

Eye level

VP

Viewpoints

A number of different viewpoints can be created with perspective drawing, depending upon where you position the vanishing point in relation to the object.

For instance, it is possible to create worm's eye views and bird's eye views of objects, and achieve some very dramatic effects by changing the position of the vanishing point.

When you are using single-point perspective drawing, decide which viewpoint will enable you to show the information or details that you wish to convey and then position the vanishing point accordingly.

Fig. 1.30 *Different effects can be achieved by moving the vanishing point in relation to the object.*

17

*In the drawing of the office block shown on the left, Costall Allen have used **two-point perspective**. It has been used to illustrate a particular project in a promotional leaflet which is sent out to potential tenants and buyers. At the same time, working drawings, including a specification, are also prepared in order to apply for planning permission, and to be used in the actual construction.*

Two-point perspective

Two-point perspective enables you to draw objects at an angle to the viewer. The horizontal lines of the object converge at two different vanishing points positioned on the horizon or eye-level line.

The series of diagrams in Figure 1.32 shows the stages involved in making two-point perspective drawings.

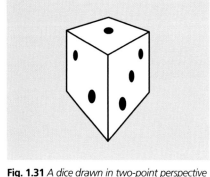

Fig. 1.31 *A dice drawn in two-point perspective*

Multiple vanishing points

Sometimes, the shape or viewpoint of some objects that you want to draw may entail the use of three or four vanishing points.

The drawing of a skyscraper building in Figure 1.33 has been drawn using three vanishing points.

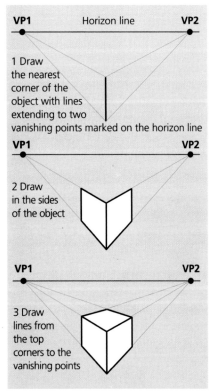

Fig. 1.32 *Stages in two-point perspective drawing*

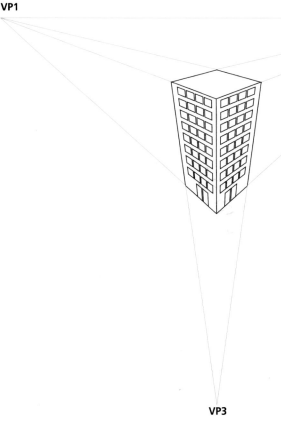

Fig. 1.33

The finished project, Doddington Court, can be seen in the photograph below.

*The publicity material for a local building project shown above illustrates the use of **multiple-vanishing-point perspective** in architectural drawing.*

The outline of the simple building in Figure 1.34 uses four vanishing points.

In a complex drawing, such as the interior of a room, it is quite possible that you might need to use several different vanishing points to enable you to draw the room and its contents in the correct perspective.

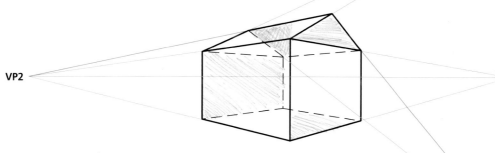

VP3

VP2

VP1

VP4

Fig. 1.34

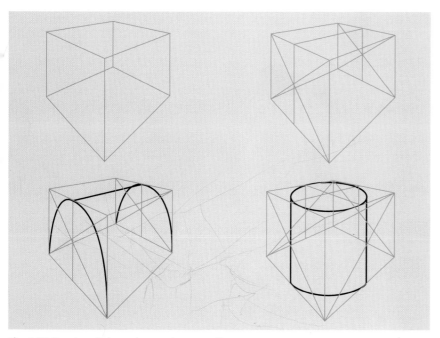

Fig. 1.35 *Drawing circles and curves in perspective*

Circles and curves in perspective

Circles and curves are simple to draw in perspective as long as you have constructed a perspective crate first. Draw the crate using either single- or two-point perspective and then draw the object within it, as shown in Figure 1.24. Draw diagonal lines on the ends of the crate to enable you to find the centre. This is where the curved surface will 'touch' the crate. Sketch in the shape of the curve, keeping it within the crate. To draw circles and cylinders you will need to find the centres of the other two sides of the crate. Lightly sketch in the outline to begin with. When you are happy with it, go over it with a darker line and then rub out the crate.

Putting it into practice

1 Make a tonal range for your pencil. Do this by shading very lightly with the pencil and gradually increasing the pressure until you have the full range of tone or shading that the pencil can produce. Label it with the grade of pencil used and then do the same thing for each graphite pencil in your case or box.

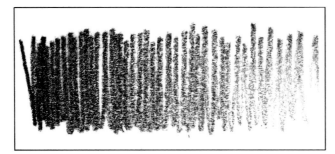

An example of a tonal range for a B pencil

2 Spend a few moments working through the exercises on page 11. Try to use them as warm-up exercises each time you begin drawing.

3 Working freehand, draw a circle and then an ellipse. Don't forget to construct a frame first and then draw the shape within it, touching the sides.

4 Choose a variety of objects from around the room you are in and make freehand oblique drawings of them. Begin by drawing crates and then draw the objects inside them.

5 Make an isometric drawing of a block which has a proportion of 3:1:1 (i.e. it is 3 times longer than it is wide or high).

6 Make a single-point perspective drawing of the interior of your bedroom, similar to the one shown below.

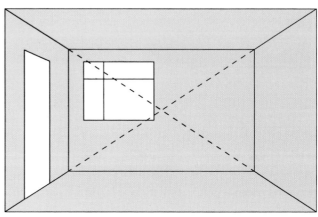

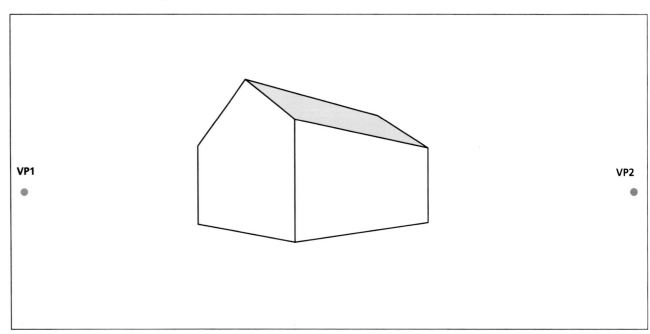

7 The drawing above shows a simple house shape drawn in two-point perspective. Copy it as carefully as you can and then add the following to your drawing: two windows, a door and a chimney. Make sure that you use two vanishing points to construct your drawing. Then, add the fine details to the drawing such as drainpipes and chimney pots, etc. When you have completed the house, add a garden, but remember to keep it in perspective.

8 Choose an object which consists of curves or cylinders and make a two-point perspective drawing of it.

9 Choose an object which contains rectangular and circular shapes within it (such as a walkman or a camera) and make a freehand drawing of it.

10 Drawing can sharpen up your observational skills. Find a natural object and make an observational drawing of it. Develop the drawing into a design that could be used on textiles or fabric.

2·Bright ideas

Clear communication is essential for successful designing. First of all, you need to clarify your own ideas for yourself so that you can develop and refine them. In school, it may be your teacher who needs to know what you are trying to do in order to help you develop your ideas. Later, you may be communicating your ideas to a client or customer, to show them possibilities that they can choose from.

When the time comes for your design to be constructed, clear communication is vital, so that the person who has to make it can understand what is required. In industry it is highly unlikely that the person who designs the product will go on to actually make it, so discussions often need to take place between the designer and the manufacturer.

In designing, graphics are a very important part of the communication process – it is far more effective to draw your ideas than trying to describe them through words. Your sketches and drawings may be used to simply show what a finished product will look like, or they may be the stimulus for discussions which lead to the development of the design by a group of people.

Fig. 2.1 *Communication between designers and manufacturers in industry*

Fig. 2.2 *Examples of a designer's sketches of ideas for a juice carton*

Fig. 2.3 *A student's design ideas for a single-seater sports car*

Whatever role your drawings play in the design process, they need to be done in such a way that they are easily recognisable and realistic. Three-dimensional drawing (as explained in the previous chapter) is one step towards realistic graphics; another is to represent the materials that are likely to be used in the making process.

This chapter will show you how to make your design ideas look more realistic. This will enable you to successfully communicate your ideas to those people who need to understand them.

SHAPE AND FORM

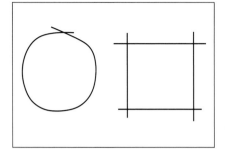

Fig. 2.4 *Lines are used to define space.*

'Shape' is 2-dimensional – a flat area that is defined by lines. Random shapes can be created by drawing lines that cross over each other, as shown in Figure 2.5. Shapes created in this way can be developed and used as decorative designs or pattern effects.

Fig. 2.5

Fig. 2.6 *Geometric shapes are not just used in design drawings – they are all around us.*

Many of the objects around us consist of geometric shapes such as squares, rectangles, and triangles. This is true in nature too (natural honeycomb, for example, consists of 6-sided hexagonal shapes). In constructional terms, geometric shapes can be used to make very strong structures. It is important to consider this when working with sheet materials such as paper, card, metal, plastic and wood.

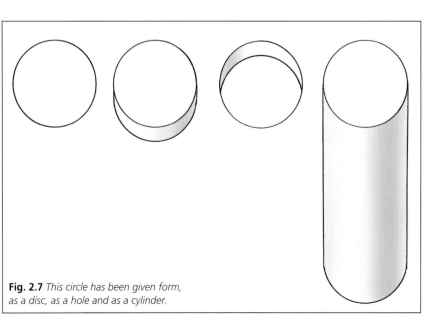

Fig. 2.7 *This circle has been given form, as a disc, as a hole and as a cylinder.*

Design ideas are often best communicated in 3 dimensions, using techniques such as oblique, isometric and perspective drawing (see Chapter 1). Three-dimensional drawing makes objects look solid and gives them 'form' as well as shape. When you portray form, you can give an impression of details such as size, proportion and weight. It is not possible to do this to the same extent using 2-dimensional drawing. Figure 2.7 shows how a simple shape can be given form in order to create a number of 3-dimensional solid forms.

Light and shade

Drawing the effects of light and shade on objects can also be used to portray form. Simple shading with a pencil will give an indication of how light falls on the surfaces of an object. Think carefully about the imaginary position of the light source in your drawing, and remember that the areas of the object that are facing the light and those nearest to it will be lighter, while areas facing away from the light, or further away will be darker.

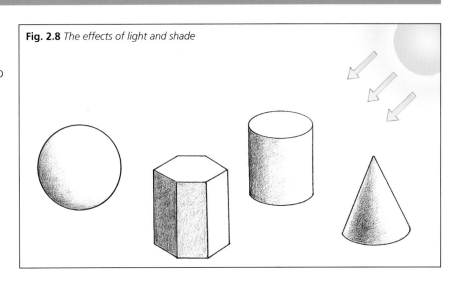

Fig. 2.8 *The effects of light and shade*

Shadows

Drawing the shadows from an object also helps portray its shape and form. Shadows can play an important part in design. For instance, architectural drawings sometimes show the estimated position of shadows because they may affect the visual appearance of the building.

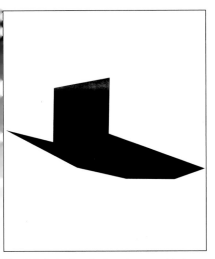

Fig. 2.9 *A shadow that portrays a cubic form*

When including shadows in a drawing it is important to remember that they also follow the rules of perspective (as explained in Chapter 1). Shadows have their own vanishing point which is normally found where a line perpendicular from the light source (LS) intersects the horizon line. This point is usually marked 'VPS' or 'vanishing point of shadow'.

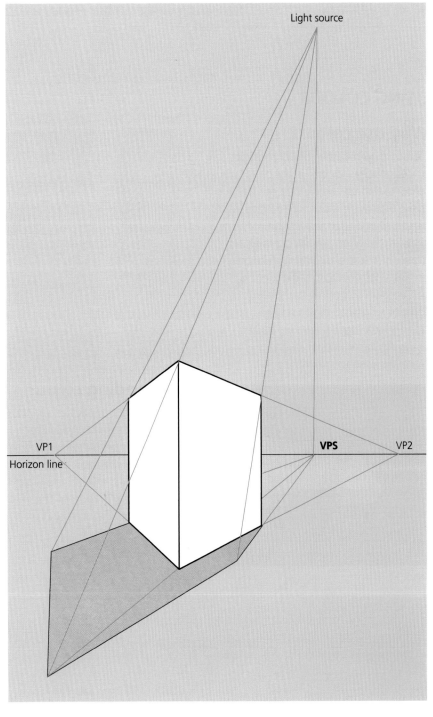

Fig. 2.10 *A shadow drawn in perspective*

Colin Plant is working towards becoming a graphic designer. He decided to pursue a career in graphic design after working in a school reprographic department and in the print room of an architect's office. To achieve this he went to college to obtain a National Diploma in graphic design, and he is now studying for a BA degree in graphic design at the University of Northumbria at Newcastle.

The poster on the right is one of several that Colin produced for his diploma. It illustrates **colour harmony** and was produced as an exercise in using gouache. The aim of the exercise was to create three distinct tones in all the colours used and to apply the colour flat and accurately. (Tones are created by adding white or black

USING COLOUR

Why use colour?

Colour is used in the communication of design ideas for a number of reasons. It might simply be used to make a drawing look more attractive, or it might be used to highlight or draw attention to specific parts of a drawing (this is explained further on pp. 30–31). And like shading, colour can be used to portray the shape and form of an object. It also makes objects look more lifelike or realistic by giving an impression of the materials used to make them.

Fig. 2.11 Colour is useful for communicating design ideas. Here it has been used to highlight a chosen idea, and to show what material the object will be made of.

Understanding colour

Using colour is not always as simple as you might first think. Applying too much colour or the wrong choice of colour will spoil a drawing. To use it to its best effect, you need to have an understanding of the theory of colour.

Natural light can be split into seven different colours (Fig. 2.12). These are called the colours of the spectrum.

They are red, orange, yellow, green, blue, indigo and violet. The colour of an object depends on how much of each of these colours is reflected or absorbed by it. For example, a red object reflects red light and absorbs the other colours. White objects reflect all colours, while black ones absorb all colours.

Colours have three elements, hue, chroma and tone. Hue describes a colour in general terms, for example red is the hue, while vermilion is the specific colour. Chroma describes the intensity or brightness of a colour and tone refers to the amount of black or white found in it.

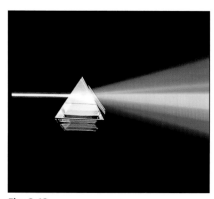

Fig. 2.12

Fig. 2.13 The tonal range of a colour

to colours, and are difficult to produce accurately.) Typefaces that look interesting next to each other were chosen to give the image an eye-catching appearance.

Another of Colin's projects was to design a poster with a 1960s theme, which is shown on the next page. After researching typical posters of the period, he decided upon a hippy poster, as the hippy movement was a prominent and popular force of the era and is still well known today. Colin also wanted to include other important and celebrated symbols and icons such as John Lennon, the yin and yang signs and Che Guevara. He used bold colours of similar shades (oranges and reds) to reflect the psychedelia craze of the 1960s, and created the rounded, friendly-looking typeface for the same reason.

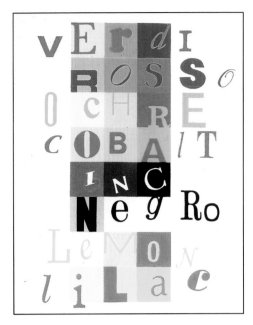

Primary colours

In design work, red, yellow and blue are known as the primary colours. This is because they are colours that cannot be created by mixing other colours together. All other colours can be made by mixing the primary colours together, in different proportions.

Fig. 2.14 *The primary colours*

Secondary colours

The three colours produced by mixing each of the primary colours together are known as secondary colours.

Fig. 2.15 *The secondary colours*

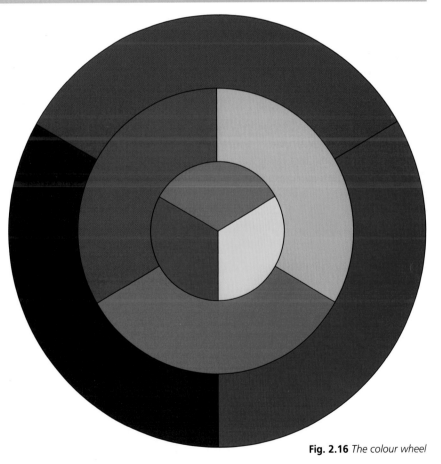

Fig. 2.16 *The colour wheel*

Tertiary colours

When a primary and a secondary colour are mixed together the result is known as a tertiary colour. Tertiary colours are subdued, earthy colours. They are useful for highlighting ideas because they allow the idea to stand out rather than the colour itself (see Fig. 2.11 on page 24).

Over the years many complex models have been devised to show the relationships between the colours. A very simple way of understanding them is to imagine the three primary colours forming the centre of a wheel. In a ring around them are the colours produced by mixing them together, the secondary colours. In

the outer ring is the range of tertiary colours produced by mixing the primaries and secondaries together. The diagram in Figure 2.16 shows this relationship very simply (e.g. red and yellow mix to produce orange), but it does not take into account the effect of tone (i.e. the results of adding black or white to a colour).

*The success and impact of this poster produced by Colin Plant are the result of the **colour interaction**, which creates discord and so grabs attention. The right-hand corner of the poster has been designed to look as if it has been torn off to reveal behind it an American poster protesting against the CIA and the Vietnam War. The lower part of the poster illustrates the use of colour harmony to create a soothing contrast.*

The brochure cover shown on the right was produced using only two colours – black and red. Fewer colours, used well, can often be more effective than using many. In this case, the theme of the brochure (vandalism) lends itself well to sparse use of stark, threatening colour. To give the image a dynamic impact and reflect the violent nature of vandalism, Colin juxtaposed the type and the logo and turned the design at an angle. After considering many typefaces, including handwritten and spray-can, he decided

THE EFFECTS OF COLOUR

Your designs, and people's understanding of your designs, can be greatly affected by the way you use colour. Some colours go well together, others don't. It is very important to remember this when using colours to help put across your ideas. The communication of good design ideas can be spoilt by a poor choice of colours.

To understand the relationship between colours and to see why they appear to react with each other we need to look at their position in the spectrum or on the colour wheel (Fig. 2.16, page 25).

Colour harmony

Colours that appear close to each other on the spectrum, such as orange and yellow, go well together and create harmony. It is important to consider this, for instance, when choosing colours for interior design. Rooms that are intended for peace and relaxation and that have to be lived in everyday need to have a harmonious colour scheme!

Fig. 2.18 *Colours in harmony*

Colour contrast

Colours from opposite ends of the spectrum can also be put together to good effect. Such colours are known as complementary colours and they create contrast. Complementary colours are used when you need to make things stand out vividly from other things around them. For instance, road signs need to contrast with the environment around them, so both shape and colour are used in their design to create visual tension.

Fig. 2.17 *Colour harmony has been used to good effect in this Liberty window display.*

Fig. 2.19 *Colours creating contrast*

to use a computer-generated type because it had sharp edges and violent, ragged strokes. He used letratone to produce the grey colour – these are in fact black dots, but the eye sees it as grey. The photograph on the right shows a colour mock-up of the final design and the two colour-separated print masters. At this stage both masters are printed black. However, when the final print is made, they are put together and the bottom right section is printed in red.

Colour perception

The way we see colour and the effect that colour has on what we see always need to be considered when you are communicating your ideas. Some colours, for example, give us feelings of warmth or cold. Yellows, oranges and reds are warm colours while greens and blues are cold colours. If you look at coloured designs, you will see that warm colours appear to come towards you from the page, while cold colours go away from you. This impression of approaching and receding colours is useful when you need to highlight ideas on a page. Warm colours are more effective for this than cold colours.

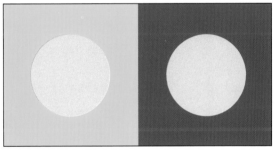

Fig. 2.21

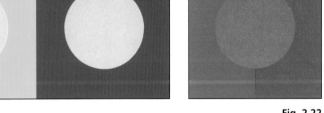

Fig. 2.22

Colours can have a similar effect on the way we perceive size and weight. Some colours, usually the warm range, can make objects look larger and heavier. This can be seen when two objects of the same size but different colours appear next to each other (Fig. 2.20).

The human eye always sees a colour in relation to at least one other colour. The way colours are seen and perceived is affected by background and adjacent colours. Look at the circles in the centre of the squares in Figure 2.21. They are both exactly the same colour, but they appear to be different because our eyes see them in relation to the background.

The way you see the grey circle in Figure 2.22 is affected by the colours either side of it. To prove this, lay your pencil vertically along the centre of the square. The circle will appear as two different shades of grey. This effect is known as 'simultaneous contrast' and is a good illustration of how the way we see colours is affected by other colours around us.

Fig. 2.20

DRY MEDIA

Coloured pencils

Coloured pencils are popular with professional illustrators and artists. They are very useful where subtle tones and colours are required, and for combining with other materials such as markers or paint. Water-soluble pencil crayons are also available. With these, when you have applied the colour to the paper, you can brush it with clean water to create watercolour effects.

Fig. 2.23 *A range of coloured pencils and an example of work using coloured pencils*

Pastels

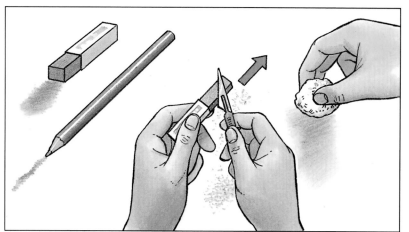

Fig. 2.24 *Using pastels for different effects and an example of pastel work*

Pastels are very versatile colouring materials. They are excellent for producing tonal effects and can create very effective and dramatic backgrounds on to which design ideas can be mounted. Pastels are available in either stick or pencil form. They can be applied directly on to paper, like chalk, or they can be painted on with cloth or cotton wool. To paint with pastels, you first need to scrape the pastel into a fine powder with a sharp knife. You then apply the powder to the paper with cloth or cotton wool that has been dipped into Clean Art fluid or a petroleum-based lighter fuel. (Take care when using flammable liquids and be sure NOT to use butane gas.) When used in this way the fluid evaporates and the powder is fixed to the paper, so it does not require a fixative spray. However, pastels that have been applied directly to the paper will need to be fixed to prevent them from smudging.

Markers

There are two types of coloured markers: water-based and spirit-based. Water-based markers are inexpensive and available in the form of felt-tipped pens, which are used for general colouring purposes. The ink is water soluble and takes a few seconds to dry, which can cause the paper to wrinkle when used to colour large areas. Felt-tipped pens are convenient and particularly useful when highlighting and colouring design ideas. Spirit-based markers are usually more expensive. They are mainly used for presentation work, often combined with coloured pencils or pastels. The use of markers is covered in more detail in 'Looking Good', the next chapter in this book.

Fig. 2.25 *Markers and an example of marker work*

WET MEDIA

When working with wet media such as watercolours, gouache or acrylics you must remember to stretch the paper before beginning work. This will prevent the paper wrinkling when the paint is applied. First of all, you need to thoroughly wet the paper with clean water, either in a sink or a tray. Then drain off the excess water and lay the paper on a clean drawing board. Now stick the paper down on to the board with gummed paper tape and allow it to dry before you use it.

Fig. 2.26 *The stages in stretching paper*

1 Wet paper thoroughly.
2 Drain off excess water.
3 Stick to a clean board with gummed tape.

Watercolour

Fig. 2.27

In design work, watercolour is used mainly as a wash to highlight areas of drawings to draw attention to them, or to create tones to portray form. It is applied as a thin transparent wash, which tints the drawing. Denser areas of colour are built up by applying more layers of the wash. Figure 2.27 shows how a series of colour washes can be applied to create a light and shade effect on a cube.

Watercolours are available in two different grades: artists' colours, which are made from high-quality pigments and are very expensive; and students' colours which are more reasonably priced and perfectly adequate for the design and technology work that you will be doing.

Gouache

Gouache is an opaque form of watercolour similar to poster paint. It is very useful when strong, dense colour is required, and is very good for painting card models. Gouache is available in jars or tubes and is water soluble, so your brushes can be easily cleaned in water even after the paint has dried on them.

Fig. 2.28

Acrylics

Watercolours and gouache have been used as painting materials for several hundred years. More recently, acrylics have also become available. They were developed in the 1930s to provide a paint that was tough enough to be used for murals in very exposed positions. To achieve this resilience the colour pigment is bound in a synthetic resin, which is made from a plastic material called polyvinyl acetate (PVA).

Acrylic paint is very versatile. It can be applied as a thin wash like watercolour or as dense, opaque colour like gouache.

It is important to remember that acrylic paint is quick-drying, so the screw tops on the tubes must be kept clean and replaced. And because it is plastic based, it is very difficult to remove from brushes if it is allowed to dry.

Fig. 2.29 *Tubes of acrylic and a novel design for a barcode, painted using acrylics.*

HIGHLIGHTING IDEAS

In the early stages of designing, your graphic work will often consist of sheets of initial ideas, quickly sketched as you have thought of them. The next stage is to highlight the ideas that you want to refine and develop further. Highlighting draws the viewer's attention to ideas. It can also be used to separate good ideas from unsuitable ones. Highlighting can be carried out in a number of different ways using line, tone and colour.

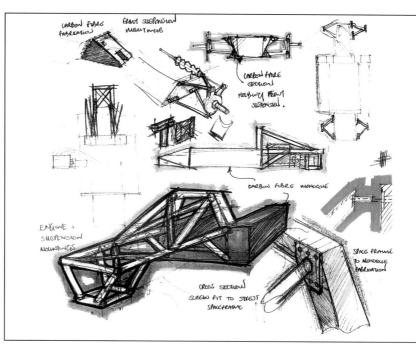

Fig. 2.30 *Highlight ideas that you want to develop further.*

Weighted line

One way of highlighting ideas is by using what is known as a 'weighted line'. This involves drawing a darker or thicker line around the outline of the drawing you want to highlight. A weighted line has the effect of lifting the selected drawing away from those around it on the page. This technique can be used on both pencil and ink drawings. When working in pencil, you need to use a softer grade to make a darker line. When working in ink, use a wider nib or pen tip. Figure 2.31 shows how a weighted line can be used.

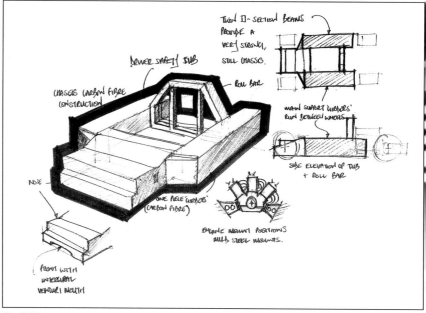

Fig. 2.31

Tone

To highlight an idea using tone, shade an area around the outline of your chosen drawing (a pencil is usually used for this). Graduated tone can be effectively created by gradually increasing the pressure of the pencil on the paper.

Fig. 2.32 *An idea highlighted using tone*

Colour

Almost any coloured media can be used to highlight design ideas. There are special pens available for highlighting text, but they are not always suitable for using on drawings because their ink is too bright. This can give an overpowering effect, with the highlighter colour standing out vividly and the idea becoming lost in the glare. The rule for using highlighter pens is to use them with care – try them out on a piece of scrap paper first.

Fig. 2.33 *Highlighter colour can be useful. Here it has been used to good effect to draw attention to part of a drawing. Be careful when using highlighter pens – do not let the colour overpower your drawings.*

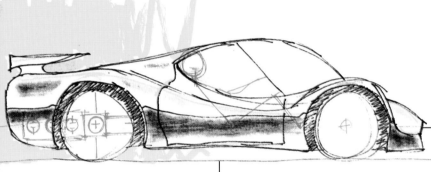

When you are highlighting an idea, choose the colour carefully. You will often find that the more subdued, subtle colours are more effective than bright ones. Marker pens, pastels, gouache, watercolour and acrylics are all suitable. The most common technique is to apply the colour around the selected idea to make it stand out (Fig. 2.34).

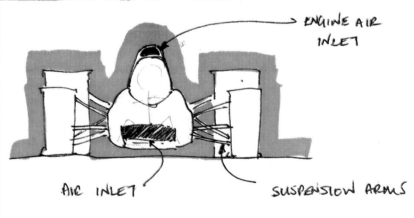

Fig. 2.34

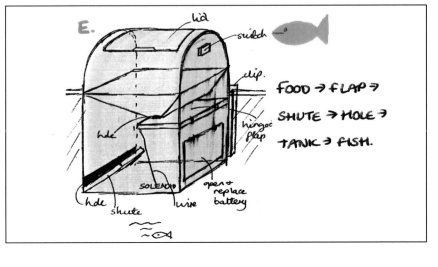

Colour can also be applied directly over an idea to highlight details such as how it is assembled or to show how it works. In this case the colour needs to be thin enough for the details of the drawing to show through. You will also need to apply colour directly to the drawing when some indication of the finished colour or the materials to be used is required.

Fig. 2.35 *Colour has been applied directly over this drawing of a fish feeder to emphasise its details.*

Martin and Mel Holliday run Chiselwood, a small woodworking company that specialises in designing and building tailor-made kitchens and fine furniture. In 1989 Martin decided to turn his cabinet-making hobby into a business, with Mel, his wife, looking after the accounting and marketing side of things. In 1991 they were named 'Small Business of the Year' by a national newspaper.

Martin produces unique individual designs which tend to have a very traditional style (a lot of Chiselwood's work is fitted into restored or converted farm buildings).

WORKING WITH INK

Ink is a very versatile medium for communicating design ideas. It can be used at all stages of design, from sketching initial ideas to technical drawing (using a technical pen). And if you use a brush to apply it, ink can be used for highlighting ideas or painting in areas of colour.

Fig. 2.36 *Ink has many uses in communicating design – from technical drawing to highlighting ideas.*

Inks

You can buy ink in a variety of colours as well as traditional black drawing ink. Some ink manufacturers produce between 15 and 20 different colours. There are also different types of ink available. For example, artists' drawing ink is waterproof and dries as a glossy film; non-waterproof inks dry to a matt finish and can be diluted with distilled water if required.

Pens

There is a wide range of pens available for drawing, from simple dip pens to the highly specialist technical pens used for technical drawing and draughting. Dip pens do not have a built-in ink reservoir, so need to be dipped directly into the ink. You can buy a large number of nibs for them to enable you to produce a variety of line widths.

Felt- and fibre-tipped pens are made with both waterproof and water-soluble inks and in a variety of thicknesses. They are a clean and convenient way of using ink.

For accurate drawing, technical pens are available in a number of line widths ranging from 0.1mm to 2.0mm. The ink flows through a delicate hollow nib which must be treated with great care. Special inks are used in technical pens – normal waterproof ink would dry and clog the nib.

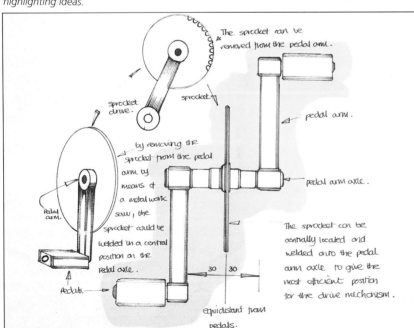

Fig. 2.37 *Inks and pens:*
a) dip pen;
b) felt-tip pen;
c) technical pen

However, he has also designed furniture with a more modern look for offices. Chiselwood try to cater for whatever the client needs, and offer a full service supplying flooring, tiles, sinks and appliances if required.

First of all, Martin establishes what the client wants. Often, ideas come from a portfolio that Martin has put together, which includes many **ink** *sketches prepared from the working drawings of previous projects (like the one shown here).*

Using a brush

You can use a brush to apply ink, either 'neat' – straight from the bottle – or diluted with water to make a wash. Different tones can be produced by adding layers of an ink wash, just as you would when working with watercolour.

Good quality brushes should be used. Traditionally, brushes were made of sable. You can still buy sable brushes today, but they are expensive, and satisfactory results can be achieved with the cheaper modern nylon brushes. Whatever brush you do use, it should be cleaned thoroughly after use (waterproof ink is very difficult to remove once it has dried).

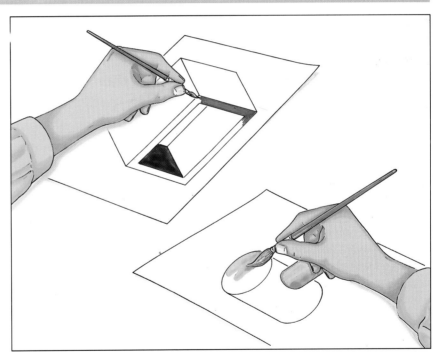

Fig. 2.38 *Ink being applied with a brush*

Ink effects

You can create a huge variety of effects when working with ink. You don't have to limit yourself to applying ink with a pen or a brush – you can use almost anything. Try making your own dip pen from a sharpened stick (take care if you use a sharp blade). You could even dab ink on with a sponge, or spatter it on using your old toothbrush!

Fig. 2.39 *Examples of effects possible with ink*

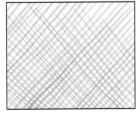
1 Lines

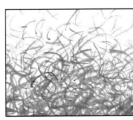
2 Cross hatching

3 Scribbles

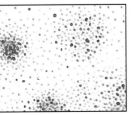
4 Dots

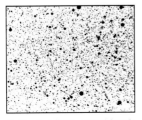
5 Spatter from a toothbrush

6 Ink wash

At Chiselwood, after Martin has had initial discussions with the client, he draws up a detailed design specification. He uses freehand sketches to show the client what is possible and produces a 3-dimensional drawing to show how the furniture may look. From this he produces a drawing showing the plan and elevations of the chosen idea. The client receives a coloured copy of the drawings, **rendered** in pencil crayon. The rendered drawing on the left shows a kitchen unit with glazed cabinets. (Chiselwood's furniture is made from a wide range of woods including maple, oak, ash and pine as well as painted finishes. The worktops are usually hardwood or granite.) If the client accepts the design, Martin produces a working

RENDERING

To make your design drawings look more realistic you can give them texture by using simple graphic techniques. This is known as 'rendering'. You can use a variety of media to achieve realistic effects and to show the materials that are to be used to make your designs. Ink, graphite and coloured pencils, pastels, paint and markers can be used either on their own or in various combinations. Some computer-graphics software packages have rendering facilities that enable products to be visualised on screen before printing out on to paper.

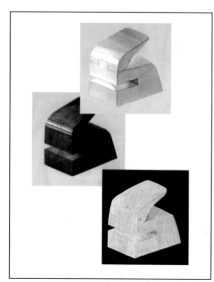

Fig. 2.40 This design for a hole punch has been rendered to make it look more realistic.

Wood

Fig. 2.41

Figure 2.41 shows a design drawing for a dice, but it is not possible to tell what it is to be made from. Simple rendering will enable you to show the materials that are to be used to construct what you have designed.

Let us suppose that the dice is to be made of wood. You can use coloured pencils very effectively to give an impression of wood grain.

Begin rendering by shading in a background colour. This should be a pale yellow or a light brown depending on the type of wood to be used. Don't forget to show the effect of light and shade by making the surface facing the light source the lightest, as shown in Figure 2.42a. Next, using a darker shade, draw in the grain of the wood. This need not be too accurate but sufficient to give an impression of grain. It is a good idea to show the end grain on one of the surfaces, as shown in Figure 2.42b.

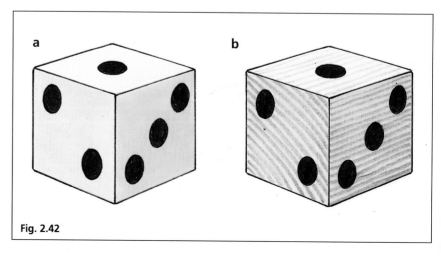

Fig. 2.42

drawing which uses orthographic projection on squared paper, like the one shown here. It will also include sections and assembly details if appropriate.

The working drawings do not need to contain every detail, as Chiselwood's cabinet makers are very experienced in what they do and can be relied upon to make the joints etc. However, details are given in full for anything that is non-standard or has unusual dimensions.

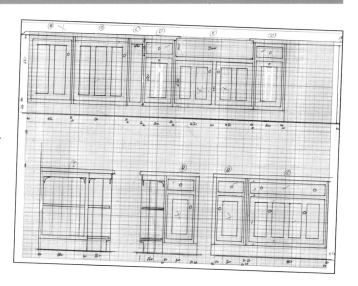

Opaque plastic

Plastic materials can be rendered using coloured pencils or markers. If you need to render a polished or reflective surface you will have to consider reflections when you show light falling on the object. Light will be reflected off the edges and corners and is rendered as highlights (these are not to be confused with highlighting ideas to make them stand out). One way to represent highlights is to leave the areas where light is reflected white and let the paper show through. Alternatively, highlights can be put in with white coloured pencil, gouache or correcting fluid.

Lines to represent reflections can be drawn on the surfaces of the material using a white coloured pencil, as shown in Figure 2.43b.

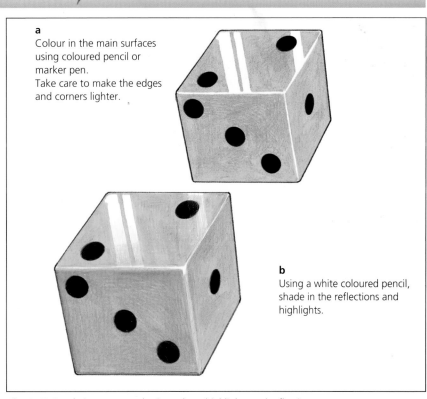

a
Colour in the main surfaces using coloured pencil or marker pen.
Take care to make the edges and corners lighter.

b
Using a white coloured pencil, shade in the reflections and highlights.

Fig. 2.43 *Rendering opaque plastic to show highlights and reflections*

Transparent plastic and glass

Transparent materials such as plastic and glass are a little more difficult to render because they have no natural colour of their own. An effective method is to use blue or green pencils to shade the surfaces, and leave areas of white paper to represent the reflections. The cube in Figure 2.44 was rendered by shading each of the six surfaces separately.

The transparent effect can be increased if you include a background in your drawing. Drawing in a background first and then rendering the object in front of it will ensure that it appears to be transparent.

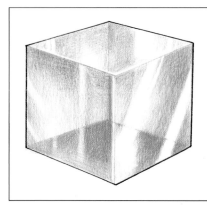

Fig. 2.44 *Rendering transparent objects*

Metal and polished surfaces

Metals with a dull or matt surface are very easy to render. First of all, you need to give an impression of the overall colour, and then show the effect of the light falling on it by varying the tones and adding highlights, as shown in Figure 2.45. As with rendering other materials, reflections can be added with a white coloured pencil, but do remember that on a matt surface they will blend into the main colour and not contrast as much as reflections on a shiny surface.

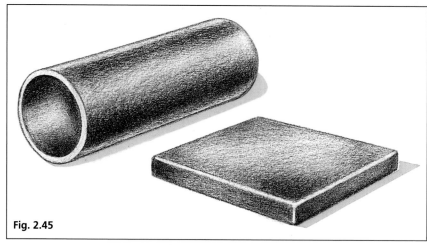

Fig. 2.45

Fig. 2.46

Highly polished surfaces and metals such as polished silver, chrome and brass do not show much of their own colour. They are rather like mirrors in that they reflect the objects around. This can make them difficult to render. Illustrators and graphic artists have overcome this problem by adopting a technique of rendering known as the 'desert landscape'. This technique involves representing the sky and the desert as if they are reflected on to the polished surface. The upper surfaces of the object reflect the sky and the lower part the ground. Figure 2.46 shows a cylinder and a sphere rendered in this way.

Step 1

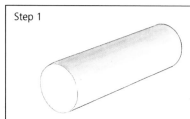

Begin by colouring in the top part of the drawing as the sky. Coloured pencils or pastels are the best media for producing a graduated effect.

Step 2

Next, working down from the horizon, fill in the ground area. Graduate the colour – start with a dark shade at the top, getting lighter towards the bottom.

Step 3

Finally, add a graduated sky effect to the end of the object and put in highlights around the edge.

Textures

The texture of a material can be effectively rendered in a variety of ways. Texture effects are particularly useful when rendering objects which have a 'rough' surface, like the ones shown in Figure 2.49.

Texture created using ink

Dry transfer texture

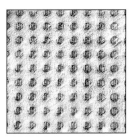
Texture created using a texture pad

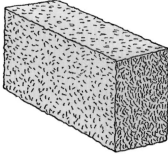

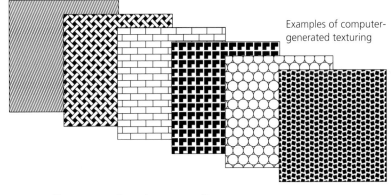

Examples of computer-generated texturing

Fig. 2.50 *Different ways of creating texture effects*

Fig. 2.49 *Textures created to show the rough surfaces of concrete and leather*

Figure 2.50 illustrates some of the methods you can use to create textured effects. You can use ink in a variety of ways (see also Figure 2.39). There is also a large range of dry transfer textures available, which can be applied by rubbing the transfer on to the drawing in the same way as instant lettering. Often, computer-graphics software has a good range of textures which are useful for rendering. Alternatively, a textured surface can be placed under the paper and then shaded over with a soft pencil.

Texture pads can be bought in a wide range of textures, but there are many objects and materials available around your house or the classroom that will work just as well. For instance, the plastic cases from old radios and tape recorders often have an imitation leather surface. Perforated metal and old speaker grills can create an effective textured look. If you are rendering a fabric surface, try a sheet of coarse glass paper under your drawing.

Place your paper over your 'texture' and rub with a soft pencil, just as if you were making a coin or brass rubbing. Try it – you will find the results are very effective.

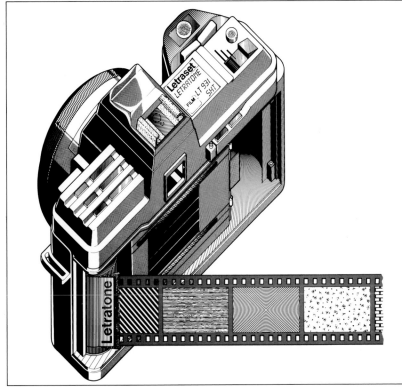

Fig. 2.51 *Illustration of a camera rendered using dry transfer textures*

Fig. 2.52 *A pupil using a textured surface for rendering*

Putting it into practice

1 Draw a rectangle approximately 150mm wide and 100mm high. Draw a number of random lines from side to side and top to bottom. Study the shapes that have been created by the lines and develop a pattern from them that would be suitable for a fabric or wall-covering design.

2 Create a tessellated pattern by repeating or fitting together geometric shapes. Colour the pattern using two colours to create a colour contrast.

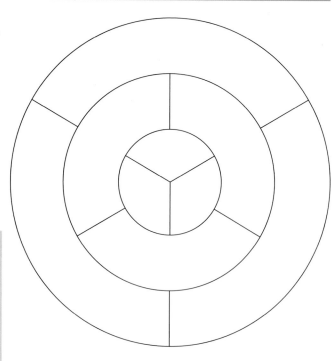

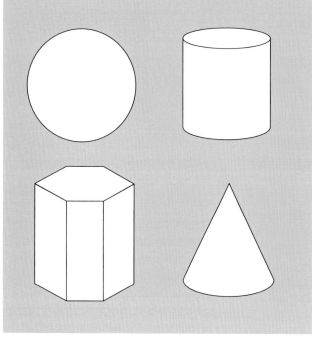

3 Copy the shapes above and shade them using a soft pencil. Mark in the position of the light source on your drawing.

5 Copy the wheel above and, using only the three primary colours, colour in the primary, secondary and tertiary colours. Mix all the secondary and tertiary colours from the three primary colours.

6 Choose a colour and, using gouache, produce a tonal range for that colour by adding black and white.

7 Draw a single-point perspective view of a room and colour it, choosing colours that create a warm and relaxing atmosphere.

8 Draw four cubes in perspective and render them to show that they are made of the following: wood, concrete, plastic and glass.

9 Using ink, produce at least six different textures that are suitable for use in rendering.

10 Copy the camera shown below and render it using a variety of different textures.

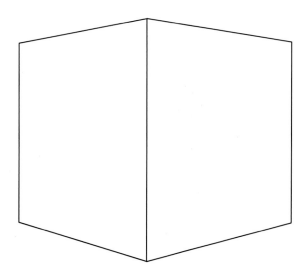

4 Copy the perspective cube shown above and then find its vanishing points. Imagine that the light source is about 6cm above and about 1.5cm to the right of the object. Draw the object's shadow in perspective too.

3· Looking good

The successful communication of your design ideas to other people will depend very much on the way you present your work. Presentation skills are very valuable throughout the design process to make your work clear and easy for you to understand, and for anybody who is going to help you to realise your design. A few simple graphic techniques can turn a page of rough initial sketches into a well-ordered part of your design drawings. This chapter will show you how to use your graphic skills to make your ideas 'look good' – an important consideration for you when presenting your work for assessment and examination.

Fig. 3.1 *Ideas rendered with markers*

In the real world too, presentation skills are crucial for selling ideas to potential clients. Customers, just like teachers and examiners, will appreciate work that is professionally presented. You are far more likely to sell your ideas (and get high marks) if your work looks good.

Fig. 3.3 *Fashion drawings*

Fig. 3.2 *An airbrushed drawing*

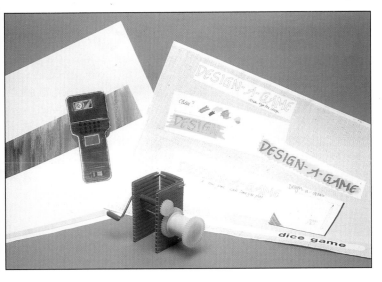

The skills described in this chapter are advanced graphic techniques – and you will need to practise to become proficient and confident in using them. Don't expect to be an expert with a marker or an airbrush the first time you use them. If your first attempts do not look like the examples shown here, do not despair. All it takes is a little perseverence – you may be surprised at the results you can achieve with a little practice.

Fig. 3.4 *Mounted work and an example of a model*

MARKERS

Spirit-based markers (also known as 'permanent' markers) are very suitable for presentation work because they have a wide range of colours and tones that dry quickly without wrinkling the paper. Some brands of markers can be matched exactly with printing inks, and paper and card colours. This enables designers to show the precise colour they propose to use.

If you do colour your drawings with permanent markers, you will need to use special 'bleed-proof' paper to prevent the ink from spreading (bleeding) over the outlines before it dries. The ink may also bleed through to the other side of the paper. Designers sometimes take advantage of this when they want to produce a pale or subdued colour. They turn the paper over and apply the marker on the reverse, allowing it to bleed through to the other side and create the effect they want.

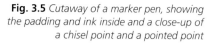

Fig. 3.5 *Cutaway of a marker pen, showing the padding and ink inside and a close-up of a chisel point and a pointed point*

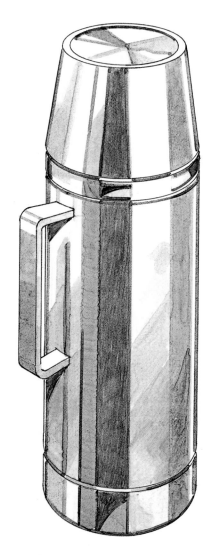

Fig. 3.6 *These objects have been rendered with markers to show that they are made from metal and plastic.*

Markers can be used on their own to present your design ideas, or they can be used in conjunction with other graphic media such as pastels or coloured pencils.

Figure 3.6 shows examples of drawings of metal and plastic objects that have been rendered using marker pens. The marker has been used to give form to the objects and to give an indication of the material they are made from. This has been achieved by using light, shade, reflections and highlights.

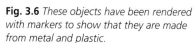

Fig. 3.7 *The high-quality rendering of this personal CD player gives it an almost photographic appearance.*

The personal CD player shown in Figure 3.7 has been rendered using a combination of markers and coloured pencils. The coloured pencils have been used to produced graduated tones on the body of the CD player and to show reflections on its surface. The highlights have been painted in with 'process white', which is a form of poster paint used by graphic designers. The fine details have been added using a technical pen (fine-line marker pens can also be used to add these finishing touches to your drawings). The finished result is a very effective drawing with an almost photographic quality. Drawings rendered in this way are often used as illustrations for brochures and advertisements – they are also an excellent way of showing people what you think your finished design will look like.

Using markers – step by step

The illustrations on this page show you, step-by-step, how to make presentation drawings using markers and coloured pencils.

First of all, you need to make an accurate drawing. The drawing in Figure 3.8 has been made using two-point perspective. You can use any method of pictorial drawing, but perspective drawing will enable you to choose the most suitable viewpoint and to produce a realistic effect. Figure 3.8 was drawn using a 2H pencil.

Fig. 3.10

Once you have blocked in the main colour, use a marker in a darker shade to create a tonal effect, similar to that shown in Figure 3.10, where darker areas have been added to help portray the form of the object. It is important at this stage that you decide where the light source will be so that you can add the tones according to its position. At this point, you can leave the main highlights as areas of clean white paper.

Fig. 3.8

In Figure 3.9, the first layer of colour has been carefully applied with a marker. When you do this it is important to use the marker quickly and to try not to overlap or leave gaps between the strokes. To begin with, you may find it helpful to hold the tip of the marker against a straight edge (be careful not to smudge the colour when you move the edge). With a little practice you will be able to apply an even layer of colour in this way. Try it out yourself first on a piece of scrap paper.

Fig. 3.11

Figure 3.11 shows the finished drawing. Reflections have been added using a white coloured pencil, and graduated tones have been incorporated by applying coloured pencils in colours that correspond to the colours of the marker ink. All that remains is to add final details with a fine-line pen and small highlights with paint.

Fig. 3.9

AIRBRUSHING

Airbrushes

Airbrushes are small spray guns that use a jet of air to spray a variety of liquid media on to paper. They can be used for colouring presentation drawings, rendering, and for painting models, and they can create very realistic effects of near-photographic quality

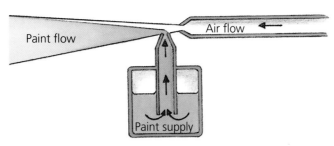

Fig. 3.13 *The airbrush principle*

Fig. 3.12 *A double-action airbrush in use*

The airbrush was invented at the end of the nineteenth century. It was first used by a doctor to spray medicine into his patients' throats. The design has changed very little over the years – it is a delicately-engineered tool that has a needle with a matching nozzle to control the delivery of paint. The nozzle must be treated with care, and the airbrush must always be kept clean and well maintained if it is to give good results.

There are several types of airbrushes available, ranging from simple, single-action brushes to more sophisticated double-action types. The single-action mechanism gives you control over the air supply to the brush and is best suited to painting backgrounds and colouring models. For more detailed and complex work, you will need to use double-action airbrushes that allow control over the paint supply as well as the air supply.

The air supply

Airbrushes need compressed air in order to work. The most economical way of providing the necessary supply of air is to use a compressor. This is an electrically-operated pump which uses either a flexible diaphragm or piston to force the air through. You can also use aerosol cans of propellant, but they only allow a limited working time before the can needs replacing and they are only useful for small-scale work or when an airbrush is only occasionally used. In order to produce good-quality work, the supply of air must be clean and should not fluctuate. Moisture in the air can also cause problems – some more expensive compressors are fitted with filters and moisture traps to clean and dry the air.

Airbrush media

Almost any liquid can be applied with an airbrush, from liquid inks and dyes to suspended pigments such as oil paint and pottery glazes. You can also buy special paints for airbrushing in a wide range of colours. These are specially formulated for easy, clog-free use. Whatever liquid you do use, do not allow it to dry in the airbrush (particularly media such as Indian ink, acrylic and oil paints). Do make sure your airbrush is thoroughly cleaned out every time you use it and washed with an appropriate solvent. The solvent should be put in the reservoir and sprayed until the liquid coming through the nozzle of the airbrush is clear.

Transparent ink   *Opaque gouache*

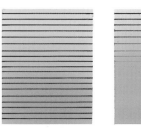

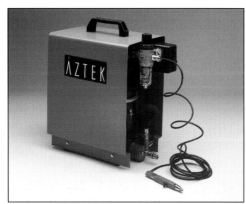

Fig. 3.14 *Cans of aerosol propellant and a compressor*

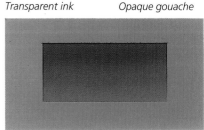

Rectangle of gouache overlaid with transparent ink

Fig. 3.15 *Examples of different airbrushed media*

42

Masking

When you use an airbrush to colour your work, you need to plan ahead carefully. With any spray technique, there is a danger of unwanted overspray. To prevent this you need to make masks to cover the areas that you do not want to be sprayed. Simple masks can be made from scrap paper or newspaper, but for more complex work, masking film or masking fluid is more accurate and appropriate. Masking film is a low-tack plastic film rather like the clear film used to cover books and posters. It is stuck over the drawing, and the parts that require colouring are cut out with a scalpel and removed. After spraying, the cut-out piece of film is replaced and other areas are removed. Figure 3.16 shows film being cut to mask an area of an airbrushed drawing. Masking fluid is a rubber-based material in an ammonia solution.

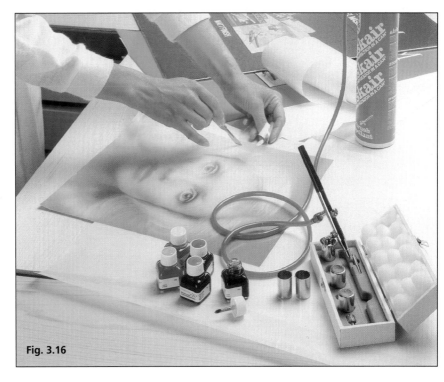

Fig. 3.16

It is painted on to the paper with a brush. The ammonia evaporates leaving behind a layer of rubber which acts as a resistant on the paper. After spraying, when the surface is dry, the rubber can be removed by gently rubbing with your finger.

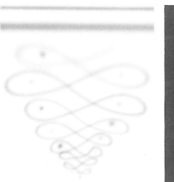

Fig. 3.17 *Airbrush techniques – lines, solid colour and graduated washes*

Airbrush techniques

Airbrushes can be used to create a variety of different effects – from thin lines, produced by spraying up to a mask or a ruler, to solid areas of colour or graduated washes. When learning to use an airbrush for the first time, it is a good idea to practise the different techniques before attempting to airbrush a drawing (see Fig. 3.17). Figure 3.18 shows you the steps towards creating a good airbrushed drawing.

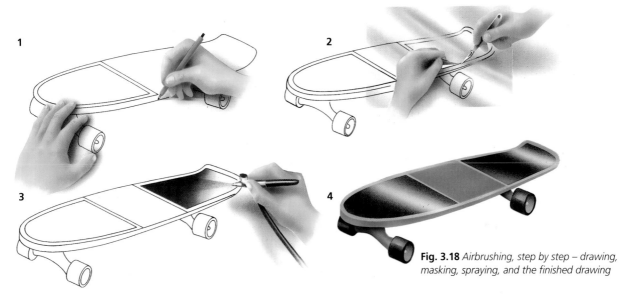

1

2

3

4

Fig. 3.18 *Airbrushing, step by step – drawing, masking, spraying, and the finished drawing*

Alona Designs was established over 100 years ago as a tailoring business. Located in a Lincolnshire village, it is now run by Bill and Maureen Atkinson and specialises in bridal and evening wear. Commissions result from a variety of sources: features and strategically placed adverts in national bridal magazines; adverts in other publications such as Yellow Pages and the Press; and personal 'word of mouth' recommendations from satisfied customers. Because business is generated in this way, Alona Designs does not need a high-profile, centrally located retail outlet.

FASHION DRAWINGS

Presentation plays a vital role in fashion design. Fashion drawings must look good and reflect the nature of the garments. The style of drawing and the choice of graphic medium influences the way information is communicated about the garment. Light and delicate fabrics, for example, need to be rendered in such a way that reflects the nature of the fabric. A design for a feminine dress would not be communicated well by a graphic style that is suited to work clothes for a factory or building site! Good fashion designs can be made to look inferior if they are not communicated in the most appropriate way.

Fashion drawings are very individualistic and often highly stylised. Designers develop their own graphic style in the same way as they develop their own fashion design style.

Fig. 3.19 Examples of professional fashion drawings

Media for fashion drawing

Fig. 3.20 These fashion drawings have been made using watercolours (left) and markers (right).

Almost any graphic medium can be used for this type of drawing, as long as it is appropriate to the design that is being communicated. Many designers prefer markers, as they are convenient and clean to use. Markers that use the Pantone colour reference system are particularly popular for fashion drawing because their colours correspond exactly to the inks and dyes that will be used to colour the fabric.

You will find examples of fashion drawings that have been made in watercolour, pastels, pen and ink, and even charcoal in most fashion magazines.

Most of Bill and Maureen's clients already have clear design ideas of their own in their mind when they first visit Alona Designs. However, they are often shown a portfolio of photographs from which to draw and develop ideas. The details of the design are decided as a result of discussions during which Bill and Maureen will establish the client's preferences. They use a variety of standard bodice, collar or sleeve designs as a starting point and adapt them to give the finished garments an individual style. The sketches on the right show various styles of necklines and sleeves, adapted from the standard designs.

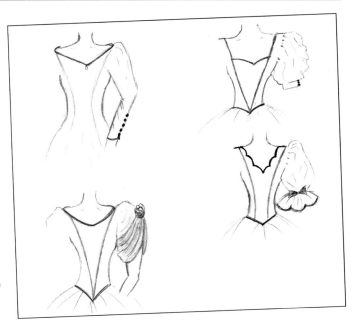

Fashion drawing techniques

Many of the graphic techniques that have already been covered in this book are suitable for fashion drawings. However, as it is a specialist type of drawing, some techniques will require further development and practice. Freehand sketching, for example, is a very important skill for most stages in fashion drawing. It is used to show design details clearly, such as folds and the fall and drape of fabrics.

Patterns and texture effects are used in fashion drawing to represent the fabric that is to be used to make the designed garment. They can be created in a variety of ways – with pencil, ink and markers. (The texture effects possible with ink are shown on page 33.) You could also use self-adhesive or dry transfer texture and pattern material, such as Letratone and Instantex. This can be expensive if you have large areas to cover, but it is quick and relatively simple to apply and gives very professional results.

Fig. 3.21 *Sketch showing folds, fall and drapes in fabric*

Drawing people

The best way to learn to draw people is to practise by sketching from a live model, but this is not always possible. A little knowledge of anatomy and the proportions of the body will help you to produce realistic drawings of people.

Although most fashion drawings are highly stylised and drawn out of proportion, it is a good idea for you to begin by drawing your figures in proportion. You can develop your own style later, when you have gained confidence in figure drawing.

The average proportion of an adult figure is 8:1, as shown on page 15. However, remember that when you are drawing children the proportion will vary according to age and stage of development. (Children's heads are larger in relation to their bodies.)

Placing a figure template under your paper will help you to draw people. You can make your own template by tracing around the outlines of models in fashion magazines. This will also help you to draw them in appropriate poses.

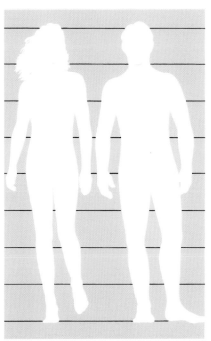

Fig. 3.23 *Male and female figure templates, against a proportioned background*

Fig. 3.22 *The use of texture in fashion drawing*

After discussing the details of the design with their client, Alona Designs produce an initial black and white design sketch in pencil on A3 paper. No colour or fabric is chosen at this stage.

Selecting the colour of the garment to be made depends upon the availability of material. Alona Designs displays samples of its wedding dresses in its showroom so that the client can look at the variety of materials, colours and textures. The final choice of material can lead to amendments in the design.

Theme boards

Many fashion designers begin work by researching and collecting information on a chosen or given theme. They then present the material they have collected on a display board known as a 'theme board' or 'mood board'. The theme board contains details about the nature of the theme, possible fabrics and colours. Possible sources of inspiration are also included. In fact, you can attach anything that you think will help you – the aim of the theme board is to capture as much information as possible about the topic for you to use when developing your ideas.

The theme board shown in Figure 3.24 was put together for a fashion project based on Switzerland. It contains a variety of material, including dried native flowers and details of traditional Swiss costume.

Fig. 3.24 *A theme board based on Swiss influences*

Developing ideas

A theme board should provide a rich source of inspiration for design ideas. Fashion designers develop many of their ideas from the material included on their boards. They produce their initial ideas as freehand sketches, which are gradually worked on and developed to ensure that they meet the requirements of the design brief. Freehand sketching at this stage must clearly show the garments' design and fabric details. The sketches in Figure 3.25 show some ideas generated from the Swiss theme board in Figure 3.24. The original sketches were done in pencil on cartridge paper and show details and some of the essential information required to make the garments.

Fig. 3.25 *Freehand fashion sketches, developed from a theme board*

Although the choice of material will affect the price of the garment, it is the labour costs that make up the major part of the price charged. Individually designed and made garments are very labour intensive. For instance, there may be a lot of hand finishing if the design is very decorative, or Alona Designs may have to purchase ready-made hand-finished lace trims, which are very expensive.

*Following the initial discussions and subsequent decisions, the initial sketch is then used as the **working drawing** for the pattern maker to produce the pattern from which the material will be cut. The photo on the right shows a wedding dress designed by Alona Designs being worn on the day!*

Working drawings

Working drawings for fashion designs are very different from those used in other areas of design and technology. Fashion working drawings are used to make the patterns for the garments. They are very simple in comparison to engineering working drawings, and they rely on the knowledge and skills of the pattern maker to interpret the details given by the designer.

Figure 3.26 shows the working drawings for a range of children's clothes. They were coloured using Pantone markers and the details were drawn in with black pen.

Presentation drawings

Presentation drawings are made to show what the final design of the garment will look like. They are produced mainly for the benefit of a client, but may also be used to provide the pattern maker with further information to work from should they need it. The presentation drawing shown in Figure 3.27 shows a range of autumn men's wear and was rendered with markers, with the details put in using a fine-line black pen.

Notice that the designer has exaggerated the proportions and made the figures look taller, and that a low viewpoint has been used, which gives a perspective effect to the drawing.

Fig. 3.27 *Example of a presentation drawing*

AUTUMN/WINTER FOR MEN!

unisex -
age 4-6
spring/summer

Fig. 3.26 *Working drawings for a range of children's clothes*

PRESENTING YOUR DRAWINGS

There is more to producing good design work than the drawings you make. You also have to present your drawings well. The way you present your designs is very important. There will be occasions when you need to 'sell' your ideas to your teacher or to an examiner. In the real world too, designers are often in situations where they have to sell their designs to clients. So, it is all-important to develop your presentation skills as well as your graphic and design skills – your work can be enhanced if presented well, and spoilt if presented badly.

Fig. 3.28 *Mounting and presenting your drawings well will improve the look of your work.*

Backgrounds

Sometimes, your presentation drawings will need to be cut out. Airbrush and marker renderings in particular can get very dirty and messy around the edges of the drawings. Cutting them out tidies them up and improves their appearance considerably. Cut-out drawings can be mounted on almost any appropriate background. You can buy ready-made graduated-colour backgrounds in paper and card, or you can produce your own using an airbrush. Streaked backgrounds can be easily made by mixing pastel powder with Clean Art fluid and applying to paper with cotton wool or a piece of lint. Photographs, photocopies and even newspaper can make good backgrounds, if they are relevant to the theme of your work. Use the background to create an effect that will enhance your work. Choose the colours carefully so that the background does not detract from the subject.

Fig. 3.29 *Examples of graduated and streaked backgrounds*

Mounting

One way of mounting your work is 'surface mounting', which entails fixing it directly on to a piece of mounting card. Take care to position your work carefully on the mount and leave a slightly larger border at the bottom. This will help to draw the viewer's eye in to the drawing and make it more pleasing to look at. When placing several drawings together on one mount, position them carefully and aim to achieve a balanced layout.

Another method is to use a 'window mount'. This is a mount that has had a hole ('window') cut into it, and your work is positioned behind the card. Window mounts require a little more skill than surface mounts, but are very effective. The window can be cut either with a sharp knife or with a special mount cutter, which you can buy from art shops. It is possible to obtain cutters that will cut circular and elliptical windows. Figure 3.31 shows the stages involved in making window mounts.

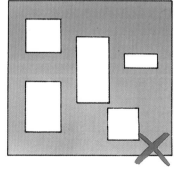
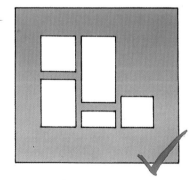

Fig. 3.30 *The way you position your work on mounts is an important consideration.*

Adhesives for mounting

When fixing your work to mounts, avoid using any glue or adhesive that will make your work too wet. Liquid glues and pastes will cause your drawings to wrinkle, and they may not lie flat when the glue has dried. Spray adhesives such as Spray Mount and Photo Mount are very good for fixing, as they allow the work to be repositioned before drying, but you must use them in a well-ventilated area to avoid breathing in any harmful fumes. Rubber-based adhesives such as Cow Gum are also effective, and have the advantage that any surplus gum can be removed when dry by gently rubbing with your finger or a putty rubber. Adhesive sticks such as Pritt Stick are good for small pieces of work, but they do not always allow for easy repositioning. Work displayed in window mounts is held in position with masking tape or drafting tape.

Dry mounting

Dry mounting is a method of mounting work that involves using a shellac-based tissue (shellac is a type of resin) which becomes sticky when heated. Special, heated dry-mounting presses are often used to mount work in this way, but it can also be done very easily using a domestic iron (take care not to burn yourself when handling a hot iron). The tissue is cut exactly to the shape of the drawing

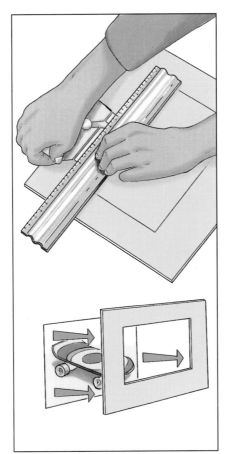

Fig. 3.31 *Stages in window mounting*

and is 'tacked' to the back of the work by touching it with the tip of an iron. The work is then positioned on the mount and covered with heatproof paper, such as brown parcel paper. The iron is put on the brown paper and the work is 'ironed'. The heat from the iron melts the adhesive in the tissue and the pressure of the iron ensures that air is removed and the work is flat.

Protecting your work

A useful way of protecting your work is to cover it with transparent material. Drawings can be sandwiched between clear plastic sheets and then heat sealed. This is known as 'laminating'. Most coloured media can be laminated without damaging them, but it is a good idea to test out a sample first to ensure that your work is not affected by heat.

Another way to protect your work is to attach overlay sheets to it. This can be easily done with most mounted work. A sheet of tracing paper or drafting film is secured to the back of the mount with tape and then folded over the front to protect the drawing. Alternatively, transparent acetate sheets can be stuck to the front of mounted work. First, the acetate sheet is cut to the same size as the mount, then a sheet of paper is placed on the acetate (the paper should be approximately one centimetre smaller than the acetate all the way round). This acts as a mask while the acetate is sprayed with adhesive. The mask is then removed and the acetate is turned over and placed on the work, as shown in Figure 3.33.

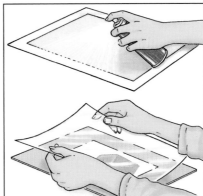

Fig. 3.33 *Protecting a drawing with an acetate overlay*

Some media are affected by prolonged exposure to light. For instance, marker pen work fades if it is left in bright sunlight, and it really needs to be protected either in a drawer or a folder. However, shutting your drawings away is not always practical, particularly if they need to be on display.

Fig. 3.32 *Dry mounting a drawing*

Alan Miller Bunford is a freelance stage designer and scenic artist. He designs and oversees the making of stage sets for plays, musicals and pantomimes for both regional and West End theatres.

*Once he has read his client's script and discussed the director's particular interpretations of the production, he sketches an outline ground plan giving a bird's eye view of the set. This will be drawn to **scale** and will give **dimensions** for the model to be constructed.*

MODELLING

Modelling allows you to see your design ideas as 3-dimensional objects. This helps you to develop your ideas and test them to see if they will work, before making the final product. Models are also a way of presenting your final ideas that is easily understood – it is easier to look at a model than to read complex working drawings. Modelling covers a range of activities, from working with paper and card models to sophisticated computers.

Sketch models

Sketch models, like freehand sketches, are used to explore design concepts and to develop ideas. They are a quick way of giving an

Fig. 3.34 *Architects discussing a model with their clients*

impression of size, shape and form, and they allow the 3-dimensional development of ideas. Sketch models can also be used to experiment with mechanisms and working principles that may be needed in a design. This type of modelling is used by designers to visualise and clarify their ideas – the models are not normally meant to be presented to the client. Almost any suitable sheet material and fasteners can be used – stiff card, paper fasteners and a variety of everyday materials are frequently used to model mechanisms.

Fig. 3.35 *Example of a simple sketch model showing a mechanism*

Demonstration models

Demonstration models are built to show other people how something works. They are very useful for demonstrating a principle or method of operation. The model shown in Figure 3.36 demonstrates how a solar heating system works.

Fig. 3.36 *A demonstration model of a solar heating system*

Some of his stage designs require extensive research, especially if the script is set in a particular architectural period. One project, a play called 'The Cemetery Club' involved investigating Jewish cemeteries in the Bronx (in New York) to ensure that the way the gravestones were represented was authentic.

The next step involves the construction of a scale 3D **model** *made out of card and balsa wood. Miniature furniture and other objects will be included in preparation for a meeting with the director. In the photo on the right you can see the model of the revolving stage set that Alan made for a play called 'Holmes and the Ripper'.*

Presentation models

Presentation models are used to show what a finished product will look like. Designers often refer to this kind of model as a 'mock-up'. A variety of different materials and techniques can be used to achieve a realistic presentation model, depending upon the nature and size of the finished product. In the car industry, full-size mock-ups of cars are made to find out what people think about the shape and style before the car goes into production. Of course, not all presentation models can be made full size (especially architectural models!), but any model should be made to scale (scale is explained in the next chapter). The full-size model of the glue gun shown in Figure 3.37 has been made so that its shape, style, and ergonomic performance can be assessed. It may only be a model of a glue gun, but a high level of realism has been obtained by the skills of the model maker.

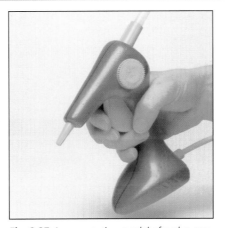

Fig. 3.37 *A presentation model of a glue gun*

Prototype models

Prototype models are made during the manufacturing stage of a product, just before the production run begins. They are not models in the true sense of the word, because they do actually work. They are created so that the 'real thing' can be tested and checked, and any final design problems can be solved, before the product goes into full production.

Computer modelling

Information technology is an important and very useful tool in the modelling process. There are many software packages available that enable you to model your designs and create 'simulations'. This process is known as 'CAD' (computer-aided design). Some CAD packages allow you to create 3-dimensional models on screen, which they then automatically convert into working drawings that can be printed out. To take the use of information technology still further, computer-aided manufacturing (known as 'CAM') can be used, whereby a computer controls the machine that is making the model. In industry, CAM is often used in the production of final products too. CAM produces very accurate and professional results.

Fig. 3.38 *A design engineer using a CAD package to produce a working drawing*

Simulation is an aspect of modelling in which test conditions can be simulated by the computer. It is used in industry when it is too expensive or too dangerous to carry out real-life testing.

Following the meeting with the director of the play, Alan Miller Bunford makes amendments to his stage-set model before preparing construction drawings from which the set will be built (you can see him preparing these drawings in the photo on the left). Detailed costings can be made at this point and he will maintain close contact with the builders throughout the set construction.

Most of the stage sets that Alan designs are for touring productions, so it is crucial that they are easy to dismantle and re-erect in a very short time. They must also be very robust in order to stand up to the constant moves.

Timber frames, covered in plywood or scenic canvas provide the background for the sets. He also uses fibreglass, expanded foam and sugar glass (for windows). All materials used, both in the

FABRICATING MODELS

Models can be made from a wide variety of materials, using many different methods and techniques. Almost any sheet material can be used. You can buy materials made especially for modelling, but scrap materials such as card and plastic from discarded packaging are much cheaper and can be just as effective.

Fig. 3.39 *Waste materials can be very useful for making models*

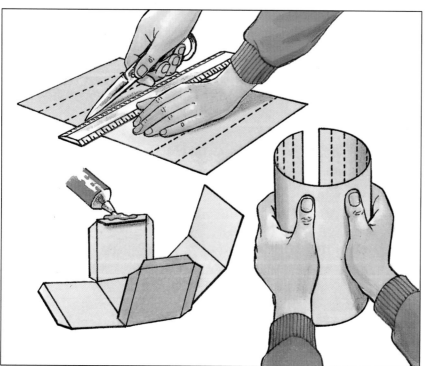

Fig. 3.40 *Using card for modelling – scoring, making a curved surface and gluing together a development with tabs*

Paper and card

Paper and card are probably the most widely used materials for fabricating models. They are relatively inexpensive and are easy to work with, using simple tools and equipment. Card should be scored before folding to allow neat, crisp edges to be formed. This can be done by running either the tip of a pair of scissors or a special scoring tool along the line of the bend before folding. Curved surfaces can be formed by scoring a series of lines and gently curving the card to the shape required.

The best way of making card models is to form them from a development with tabs added to enable the model to be securely fixed (developments are explained in detail in the next chapter).

construction and painting of the set, and the moveable objects (such as furniture) must be fire-retardant or non-combustible. Alan usually has a separate budget to provide furniture, floor covering and special props.

On occasions, Alan has also designed and cut out costumes for a production. For a play called 'The Red Barn' he produced 50 costumes, including the gentlemen's toppers. Making stage costumes is very different from making everyday garments – they are 'built', not tailored, and they need to be built to enable quick changes, with velcro for fastenings; false fronts to waistcoats and shirts, etc.

Alan's projects have included sets for a pop concert, Tupperware conference, Police Crime Prevention stand, and painted cloths for the Edinburgh Festival Theatre. The photo above shows the actual set for 'Holmes and the Ripper'.

Plastic materials

Foam board, Corriflute and Plasticard are plastic sheet materials that are useful for model making. They allow construction in a similar way to card, but they are stronger and more hard-wearing, and do not warp or distort in a damp atmosphere.

Foam board

Foam board is made from extruded foam polystyrene, sandwiched between thin layers of white ABS plastic. It is easily cut with a saw or a modelling knife and its smooth surface allows application of most paints and varnishes.

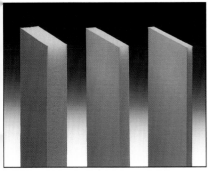

Fig. 3.41 Foam board

Corriflute

Corriflute is polypropylene sheet which is reinforced inside with flutes, rather like corrugated card. It is strong, light and colourful and can be easily cut with a modelling knife or saw.

Plasticard

Plasticard is styrene sheet which can be cut with a small saw or sharp knife and can be joined using polystyrene cement. Liquid cement such as 'liquid poly' is the most effective, as it can be applied very accurately with a small brush. Plasticard is available in plain flat sheets and embossed sheets, which represent a variety of surfaces including bricks, tiles, paving slabs and timber.

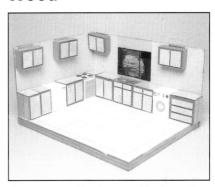

Fig. 3.43 Plasticard sheets and suitable adhesive

Fig. 3.42 Models made from Corriflute

Wood

Fig. 3.44 Wood has been used in the making of this model kitchen

A variety of natural wood and wood products can be used for modelling. Lightweight sheet material such as balsa and thin ply are most commonly used by model makers. Hardboard and MDF (medium-density fibre board) are also suitable. To join pieces of wood together, use PVA glue, hot melt glue, nails, pins or staples. Wooden models can be finished using paint or varnish. Take care that dusty materials such as MDF are only sanded in well-ventilated areas.

MODELLING FROM SOLID MATERIALS

The basic form of a model can be created by 'block modelling', using solid materials. Styrofoam, plaster, clay, plasticine and papier mâché are all suitable for solid modelling.

Styrofoam

Styrofoam is a high-density expanded polystyrene foam that is clean and safe to use. The easiest way to cut it is to use a hot wire cutter, but you can also use a hand saw, vibrating saw or bandsaw. Styrofoam does not generate dust or toxic fumes when being cut and is easy to sand with fine glass paper or 'wet and dry'. To give it a suitable surface for painting, cover the Styrofoam with a thin layer of a solution made from plaster, PVA adhesive and water, allow it to dry and then sand the surface. Remember to take care when sanding plastic materials such as Styrofoam – always work in a well-ventilated area and avoid inhaling dust and fumes.

Plaster, clay, plasticine and papier mâché

The best way to construct models made from plaster, clay, plasticine or papier mâché is to build them over a framework structure (known as an 'armature'). The skeleton frame is usually built on a baseboard of wood and then covered with chicken wire to support the modelling material. Using an armature reduces the amount of modelling material required and so reduces the weight and cost of the finished model.

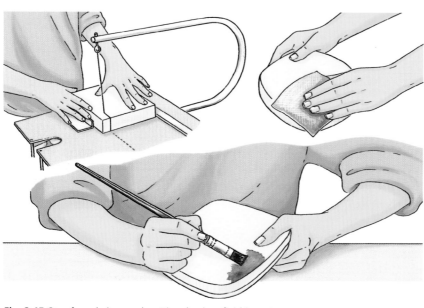

Fig. 3.45 *Styrofoam being used, cutting shaping, finishing, etc.*

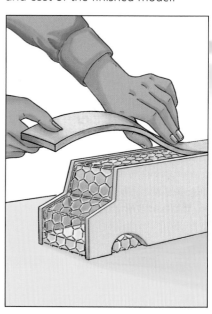

Fig. 3.46 *Using an armature for modelling with clay*

MODELLING WITH KITS

Modelling kits are very effective for communicating mechanical ideas. The advantages of kits over other materials are that they can be assembled quickly, dismantled after use, and used again and again. Lego, Fischer Technik and Meccano kits are the more popular kits that are used for this purpose. Meccano is perhaps the most versatile, but it does take longer to assemble as it requires the use of nuts and bolts. Modelling kits are not normally used for presentation models, but they are widely used for sketch modelling, especially when mechanical systems are involved.

Modelling accessories

Models can be made to show a great deal of detail and look very realistic by using specialist modelling accessories. A wide range of architectural and interior design components is available from model-making suppliers. These include scale figures, household fittings, trees, fences and cars.

Gears, motors and wheels and other details used in demonstration modelling are difficult and time consuming to make from scratch, and these can also be bought from model-making suppliers.

Fig. 3.47 *Modelling accessories, gears and motors*

Putting it into practice

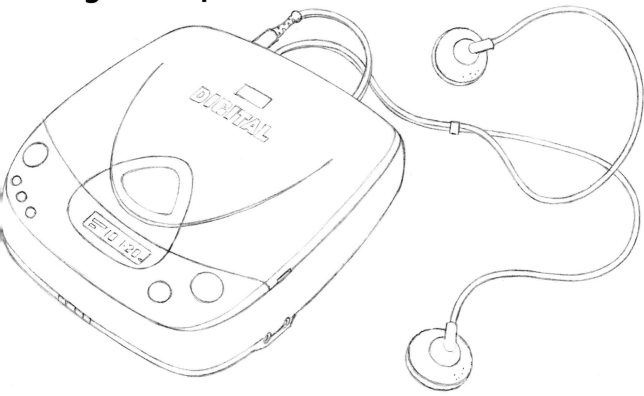

1 Copy or trace the drawing of the personal CD player above and render it using either markers or an airbrush.

2 Using a sharp knife or a scalpel on a cutting board, cut out your drawing. Make a streaked background using pastels and clean art fluid, and then paste your drawing on to it.

Producing a streaked background

3 Using a mount cutter or a sharp knife, cut out a window in a sheet of mounting card and mount your drawing behind it. Hold it in place with adhesive tape.

4 Using a block of Styrofoam or balsa wood, make a presentation model of the CD player. Paint the model using a colour scheme that will make it attractive to young people.

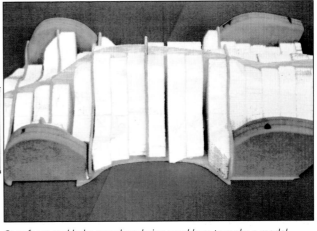

Styrofoam and balsa wood are being used here to make a model of a car.

5 Using thin card, design and make a package for the CD player. Use clear plastic to make a window so that the product can be seen.

Safety note

Take care when using tools with sharp blades such as knives, mount cutters and scalpels.

Always ensure that you use clean art fluid in a well-ventilated place.

4·Drawings to work from

The company known today as European Gas Turbines Ltd (EGT) began its life in 1946 when a small team of engineers who had worked closely with Frank Whittle (the pioneer of the jet engine) began work on the first Ruston industrial gas turbine engine.

Today, the company designs and makes a wide range of industrial gas turbines and turbochargers. Turbochargers use the energy of engines' exhausts to increase power output and lower fuel consumption.

The photograph on the left shows an example of one of EGT's turbochargers, which are used to enhance the performance of diesel engines in a wide range of rail, marine and industrial applications, including high speed trains and the SeaCat Hoverspeed, as shown here.

TECHNICAL DRAWING

Technical drawings show you how to make things that have been designed. They are used to give precise information about the materials to be used to realise the design, and its exact size and shape. Technical drawings must be accurate and precise so that what is shown in the drawing can be clearly understood and made. It is important to remember that other people, as well as yourself, need to be able to understand what you have drawn, especially if they are going to help you make what you have designed. Well-thought-out drawing will lead to straightforward, problem-free making. Technical drawing is an important part of the designing process, and it allows the designer to finalise construction details and check important measurements before making begins.

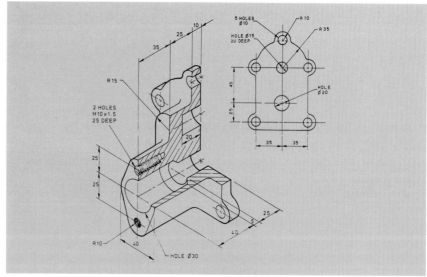

Fig. 4.1 *An example of a technical drawing of a pump cover*

Drawing instruments and equipment

Because a high level of accuracy is required for technical drawing, you will need to use appropriate drawing instruments and equipment to enable you to work precisely. Freehand drawing techniques are not suitable.

Technical drawings are usually made on cartridge paper or tracing paper, which is held securely on a drawing board to prevent the paper moving while the drawing is being made. There is a wide variety of drawing boards, ranging from simple boards to more complex drafting machines. You must always protect and look after the surface of your drawing

board. Damage caused by careless use of compasses or modelling knives will make it very difficult for you to draw accurately. And always avoid the temptation to scribble on the board in an idle moment – that too can damage the drawing surface as well as making it look unsightly.

Simple drawing boards may be made from strips of wood joined at the back with battens, or from a solid piece of plywood or similar manufactured board. They are often edged with a hardwood such as ebony to provide a perfect guide for working with a 'tee square'.

Fig. 4.2 *A drawing board, which has a rack and pinion system to enable smooth and accurate control of the 'parallel motion'*

Paper can be fastened to wooden boards with gummed tape or spring clips. Spring clips are best because they can be used over and over again and do not damage either the paper or the board.

Fig. 4.3 *Use clips or gummed tape to fix paper securely to a drawing board.*

When working on simple drawing boards, horizontal and vertical lines are drawn using a tee square. The square is held firmly against the edge of the board and used as a guide. Good quality tee squares are usually made from hardwood with either ebony or plastic 'blades'. A hole is normally cut in the end of the blade so that it can be hung up when not in use to prevent it from bending or warping.

Plastic drawing boards, like the one shown in Figure 4.5 are available from most drawing equipment manufacturers. They have many advantages over the more traditional boards. They are light and easy to carry, and have a special paper clamping device which does away with the need for tape or clips. The major advantage of plastic boards, however, is that they have a 'parallel motion', which removes the need for a tee square. The parallel motion is a special ruler that slides up and down slots in the sides of the board. The slots keep it at right angles to the edge of the board, allowing horizontal lines to be drawn very easily.

Drawing tables like the one in Figure 4.6 are often used in drawing offices or studios of schools and colleges. The drawing board has a parallel motion which is operated by a wire and pulley system on the back of the board. When not in use the board can be folded away and the table put to other uses.

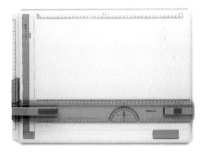

Fig. 4.5 *A plastic drawing board with a parallel motion*

Drafting machines are large drawing tables fitted with a special drafting head (Fig. 4.7). The drafting head consists of two straight edges at right angles to each other on an adjustable arm which can be moved accurately in either a horizontal or vertical direction.

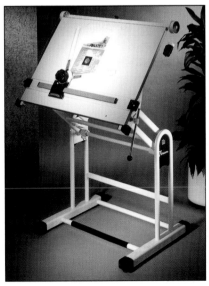

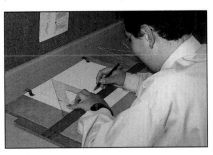

Fig. 4.4 *Using a tee square*

Fig. 4.6 *Drawing table with foldaway board*

Fig. 4.7 *A drafting machine*

At EGT, **technical drawing** is a very important part of the designing process. The photograph on the left shows a design engineer using a range of drawing-office equipment, similar to that available in schools for technical drawing. Using such equipment helps the design engineer to draw to the degree of accuracy and precision that is vital to ensure that what is shown in the drawing can be clearly understood and go on to be made.

On the right is a photo of a journal/thrust bearing from a turbocharger, along with a dimensional drawing for it. The drawing shows the size of the component and the material to be used – this particular component is made from an alloy of 94 per cent aluminium and 6 per cent tin.

ANGLES AND CURVES

Set squares

Set squares are one of the most useful drawing aids for technical drawing. They are transparent plastic triangles which, when held firmly against a tee square or parallel motion can be used to draw lines at angles. For most of your work, you will need two set squares, a 30/60° square and a 45° square. The basic angles that can be obtained with set squares are 90°, 60°, 45° and 30°, but other angles can be drawn by placing squares edge to edge on the paper. For example, a line can be drawn at 75° by placing a 30° square next to the 45° one, and so on (see Fig. 4.8). Adjustable set squares are also available (as the name suggests, they can be adjusted and set at the angle you require).

Protractors

Protractors are used for measuring and constructing angles. They are made of transparent plastic and are marked in degrees. The most commonly used protractors are marked from 0° to 180°, but there are also circular ones, which measure up to 360° (Fig. 4.9).

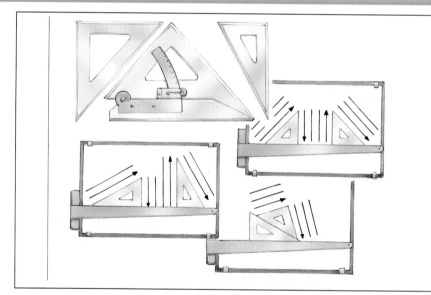

Fig. 4.8 *The range of set squares and their uses*

number of curved shapes which can be drawn around. A 'flexicurve' is a flexible strip of plastic that can be bent to any shape of curve. Flexicurves are constructed with a lead and spring steel core which allows them to be bent and re-bent as required.

Fig. 4.9

Curves

There is a variety of drawing instruments that you can use to draw curved lines. French curves are made of plastic and are available in a

Fig. 4.10 *French curves and a flexicurve*

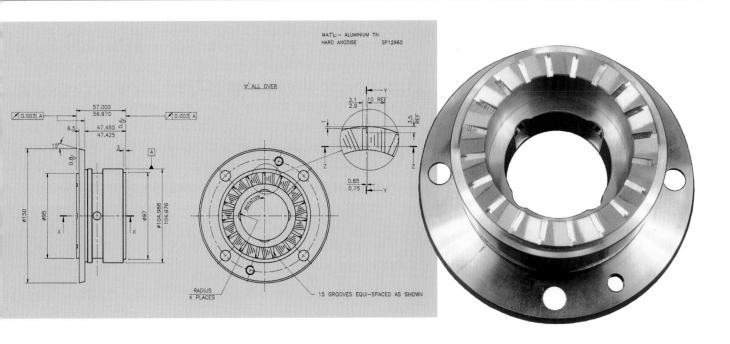

Templates

Templates are often used as guides for drawing shapes. When making technical drawings they can save you a lot of time. Templates are usually made of plastic, in different shapes or with shapes cut out which can be drawn around. There is a vast range of shapes available, from simple circles and ellipses to symbols and human figures.

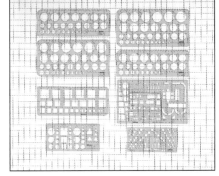

Fig. 4.11 *Templates*

Compasses

Compasses are mostly used for drawing circles and arcs, but they can also be used for constructing shapes, and dividing lines and angles. There are many types of compasses available (Fig. 4.12) but the best ones for technical drawing are the spring bow type, which are adjusted by a screw mechanism and once set do not slip. Large circles are drawn with beam compasses, where the centre point and the pencil are adjusted and then locked on to a bar or beam.

Fig. 4.12 *A range of compasses*

Cleaning equipment

Drawing instruments and drafting aids must be kept clean or they will dirty your drawings. Tee squares, parallel motions, set squares and templates should all be cleaned regularly. You can do this with one of the special art cleaners that are available or lighter fuel. Always remember to take great care when using flammable liquids and observe the special safety instructions on the container. Cleaning with soapy water is an alternative, but it is often messy and not always convenient. Drawings can be cleaned up with a paper cleaner or a putty rubber.

Fig. 4.13 *Here, a putty rubber is being used to clean up a drawing.*

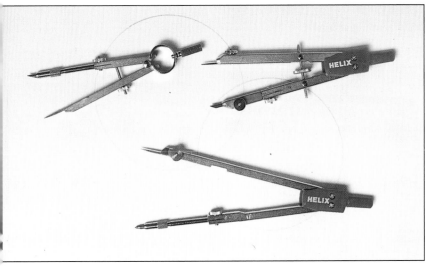

*Most of EGT's drawings are computer generated. Increasingly nowadays, **information technology** is used to produce technical drawings. The process is called **computer-aided design (CAD)**. Many of EGT's designs contain a great deal of repeated shapes. Using CAD, the design engineers can organise their work so that shapes and parts can be drawn once, stored and then recalled as many times as required. This obviously improves efficiency and productivity because it allows standard geometric shapes, text, components, drawing sequences, design layouts and assemblies to be repeated easily and quickly. This, of course, is far quicker than traditional technical drawing, whereby the same thing would have to be drawn over and over again by hand, usually by tracing.*

USING INFORMATION TECHNOLOGY

More and more, technical drawings are made using information technology (IT). IT enables you to create drawings on the computer screen, save them to the computer's memory or on to a floppy disk and then print them out on to paper later. There are many advantages to working this way. For instance, drawings do not have to be redrawn completely when alterations are made – all you have to do is retrieve your original drawing from where you saved it and then carry out the necessary changes. Storing drawings is easy and efficient. Large drawings take up less space on a disk than they do in a plan chest or folder. Libraries of frequently used symbols or components can be built up and used in a drawing whenever required.

Computer images for technical drawings are produced using a process called 'vector drawing'. A vector is a line that has a particular size and direction, and the drawing is plotted as a series of points joined with straight lines. Even circles are drawn in this way. Computer graphics software speeds up the drawing process by allowing lines to be repeated or redrawn as required. Dimensioning is also made easy – arrows can be automatically put on the end of dimension lines and measurements can be added to the drawing according to whatever national or international standard has been preset. Images can be enlarged, reduced, rotated or flipped simply by selecting an option shown on the screen.

Software packages

There are drawing packages available for most types of computers. Packages such as *AutoCAD*, *EasiCAD* and *Design View* are used on IBM PC machines, *Designer* on Acorn machines, and *MacDraw* and *Claris CAD* on Apple Macintosh machines. A lot of the 'works' packages such as *Claris Works* are also capable of fairly sophisticated drawings.

Software packages make drawing easier but they do not take away the need to be able to understand technical drawings. The computer only *aids* the drawing process – you still need to plan and think carefully about the drawing yourself. The computer will not do it for you.

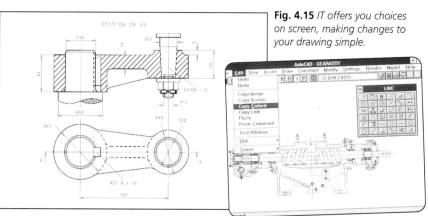

Fig. 4.15 *IT offers you choices on screen, making changes to your drawing simple.*

Fig. 4.14 *A computer-generated technical drawing*

Fig. 4.16 *Common software packages*

Also, because approximately 60 per cent of all engineering components are symmetrical, and CAD allows design engineers to reproduce mirror images of their drawings, only half of most components need to be drawn in the first place.

Another benefit of using CAD is that the designed objects can be represented on screen in 3 dimensions, which enables the designers at EGT to evaluate and check components for performance and technical accuracy. The photograph on the right shows an impeller from a turbocharger represented on screen.

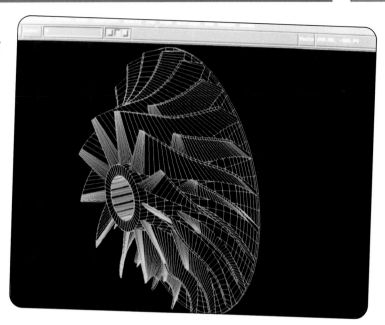

Inputting information

When you use a computer for making drawings, you need to feed information into it so that it knows what you want to draw. This information is input using a variety of devices. You can draw directly on to the screen using a mouse or trackerball. Sometimes a graphics tablet is used, which is a device that senses the pressure while you are drawing and feeds information to a 'puck' on screen to accurately reproduce the drawing.

Fig. 4.18 *Using a graphics tablet*

Fig. 4.19 *Using a trackerball*

Producing 'hard copy'

Drawings made on a computer are not printed out on to paper until they are finally complete and ready for use. The printed drawings are known as 'hard copy'. Simple dot-matrix printers are not particularly suited to outputting computer-generated technical drawings because the quality of the printout is not usually good enough for the detail needed. Small drawings (e.g. A4 and A3 size) can be printed very

successfully on both ink-jet and laser printers. Larger drawings are best printed out using a plotter. This is a device which draws the image with a pen. Small plotters are usually the 'flat bed' type with the pen held by a moving arm. In industry, larger 'roller bed' plotters are more likely to be used. Drawings can be plotted on to paper, card, tracing paper, drafting film or even plastic sheet.

Fig. 4.20 *Using an A3 plotter*

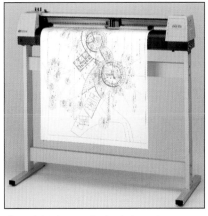

Fig. 4.21 *A large roller bed plotter in use*

Fig. 4.17 *Drawing directly on to screen using a mouse*

Designers at EGT find the ability to view on screen in 3 dimensions invaluable – it means that they can consider alternative designs without having to spend a lot of time making solid models. The drawing on the right shows part of the printout from the screen shown on page 61.

The illustration on the left is a rendered version. The ability of EGT's CAD system to produce different types of drawings helps the design engineer to make design decisions. The photographs on the right show a close-up of the finished component and someone inspecting it to ensure quality control.

STANDARDISING DRAWINGS

In industry the person who has made the drawing very rarely actually makes the product that has been drawn, and often component parts of a product are made in different countries and brought together for assembly. It is, therefore, essential that drawings which are to be used as instructions to make things can be easily understood by those who use them – misinterpretation of a working drawing could prove to be very expensive for a manufacturer. In order to overcome this, drawings made in Britain are produced to British Standards. These have been set out by the British Standards Institution (BSI) and provide a set of rules on how drawings are to be done. The rules appear in a booklet known as 'BS 308'. Schools and colleges often work to an abbreviated edition of this, known as 'PP 7308, Engineering Drawing Practice For Schools and Colleges'. The examples provided here are taken from this booklet. The British Standard provides a 'language' of drawing which is easily understood by designers and manufacturers. The same standards apply to all working drawings regardless of whether they are produced on computer or by hand on a drawing board.

Fig. 4.22 *British Standards Institution booklets*

Layout

PP 7308 includes rules on how to set out a drawing. A title block should be included at the bottom of the sheet or on the lower right-hand side. This block should contain the information required to enable the drawing to be understood. Your name and the date need to be included in the block, along with a symbol to show the form of projection you have used (projection is dealt with later in this chapter), the scale used, the title of the drawing and the drawing number.

Drawings are made in either portrait format or landscape format. Portrait is when the longest side of the drawing is vertical (the shape normally used when painting portraits) and landscape when the longest side is horizontal (the shape normally used when painting landscapes).

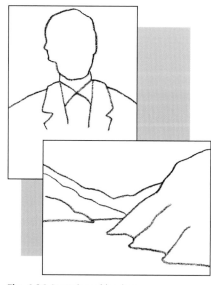

Fig. 4.24 *Portrait and landscape*

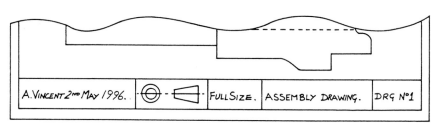

Fig. 4.23 *A typical title block*

EGT use information technology not only for designing components – CAD also enables them to visualise complex plant layouts and detect possible clashes of components, and the computer-generated images it produces can be used to enhance their publicity material.

Nowadays, designers everywhere are using 3-dimensional CAD systems to design products as diverse as shoes, cars and telephone handsets, as well as a multitude of individual components for large equipment like those made at EGT.

Scales

Drawings of objects that would fit on to the paper are known as 'full size' (they are drawn to a scale of 1:1). However, the objects you draw will not always fit easily on to the paper. If an object is too large you will need to draw it smaller than its real size, using a reduction scale (e.g. an object drawn half its actual size is drawn to a scale of 1:2).

The reduction scales recommended by the British Standards Institution are 1:2, 1:5, 1:10, 1:20, 1:50, 1:100, 1:200, 1:500 and 1:1000. If an object is too small for the details to be seen, you will need to draw a larger version, using an enlargement scale. Sometimes only part of an object needs to be enlarged and is shown in a separate view on the same drawing. The recommended enlargement scales are 2:1, 5:1, 10:1, 20:1, and 50:1.

Fig. 4.26

The scale you use depends on the size of the paper available and the size of the object you are drawing, but it should always be a scale that allows information to be easily and clearly seen. Also, the scale used should always be stated clearly on the drawing in order to avoid misunderstandings. Without a scale indicated, the house in the drawing in Figure 4.26 could be a dolls house or a real house!

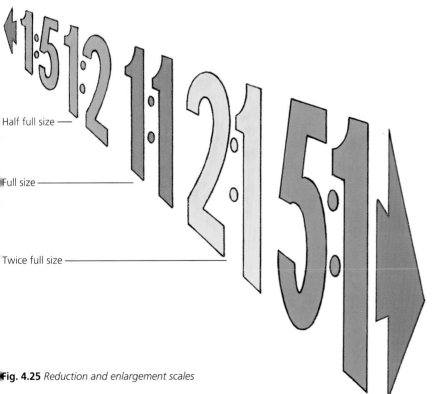

Half full size

Full size

Twice full size

Fig. 4.25 *Reduction and enlargement scales*

ORTHOGRAPHIC PROJECTION

Orthographic projection is a method of showing 3-dimensional objects in 2-dimensional drawings. The objects are drawn from three different views, known as the plan (the view from the top), front elevation (from the front) and end elevation (from the side). Orthographic projection is used in most working drawings of 3-dimensional objects.

In terms of geometry, orthographic drawing uses two planes of projection – the horizontal and the vertical plane. The object is drawn as if it is projected on to these planes. The planes intersect as shown in Figure 4.27, producing four quadrants (angles). Imagine that the object to be drawn is placed in one of the quadrants and the views projected on to the planes.

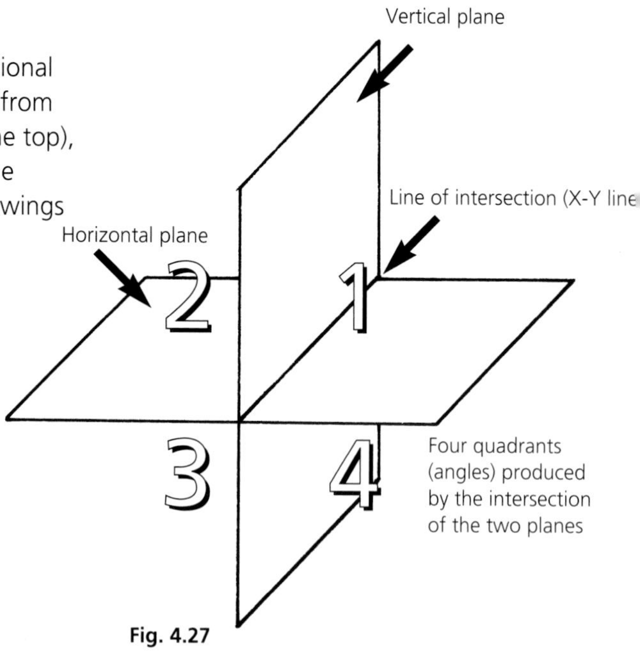

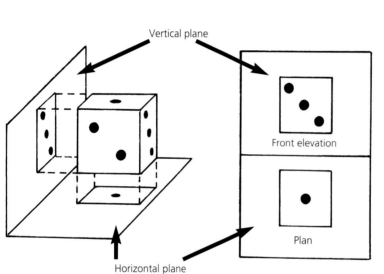

Fig. 4.27

Although four quadrants are produced by the intersection of the two planes, only the first and third are used in orthographic drawing. This is because the views in the second and fourth angles overlap and would be difficult to draw and interpret clearly.

The drawings in Figure 4.28 show a dice which ha been drawn in the first angle. The front elevation i projected through the dice (i.e. ignoring the rest o the dice) against the vertical plane and the plan is projected against the horizontal plane. The drawing is then made as if the two views are folded flat at the intersection of the two planes to create one drawing with two views of the dice.

Fig. 4.28

Drawings of objects in the third angle are made in a similar way, except that the drawing shows what you would see if you looked through the vertical and horizontal planes at the object. Third angle projection was originally used in North America and is sometimes called 'American Projection'. It is becoming more widely used in Europe and may well become the international standard. Pages 66 and 67 explain first angle projection and third angle projection in more detail.

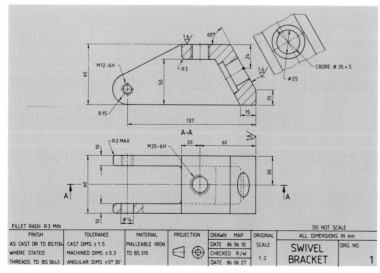

Fig. 4.29 *An example of a first angle orthographic drawing*

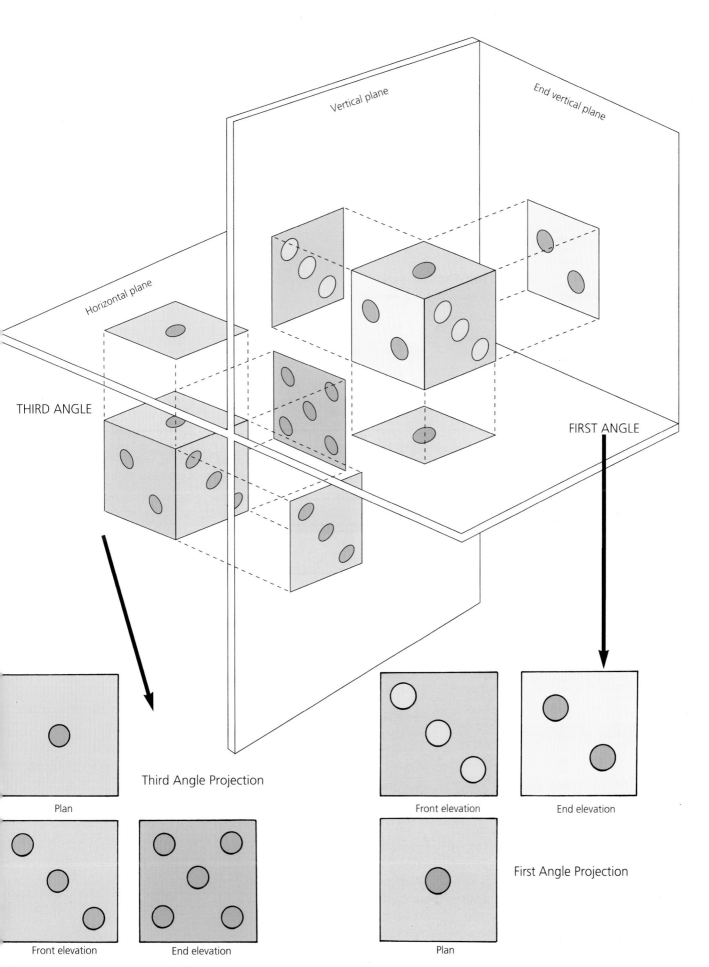

Fig. 4.30 *First and third angle orthographic drawing*

Vertical plane

End vertical plane

Horizontal plane

THIRD ANGLE

FIRST ANGLE

Third Angle Projection

Plan

Front elevation

End elevation

Front elevation

End elevation

First Angle Projection

Plan

FIRST ANGLE PROJECTION

The illustration in Figure 4.31 shows a pencil sharpener with arrows indicating the position of views to be drawn in first angle orthographic projection. You will see that, though they are not all indicated, there are six possible views that could be drawn if necessary. However, only three or four views are usually drawn, depending upon the details that need to be shown. When making a first angle drawing, always begin with the front elevation because that will determine the layout of the rest of the drawing. Some objects do not have an obvious front elevation so you will just have to choose one to work from. Position the front elevation on a faintly drawn line which represents the X–Y line of the quadrant.

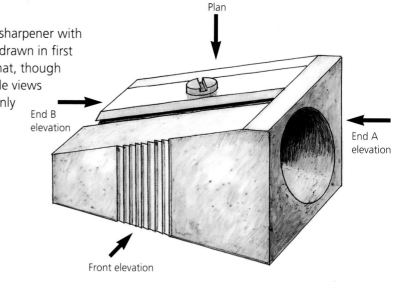

Fig. 4.31

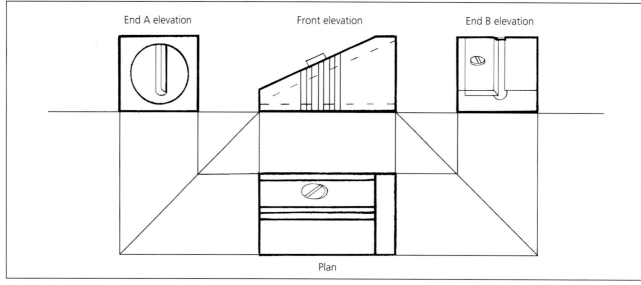

Fig. 4.32

Next, draw elevation A, as shown by the direction of the arrow in the diagram. In first angle projection, this elevation is projected through the object, as represented by the front elevation, and drawn on the left-hand side of the page. This can be seen in Figure 4.32. The same principle applies to end elevation B, which is drawn on the right-hand side of the page. Position each end elevation the same distance away from the front elevation. At the two bottom corners of the front elevation, draw a line at 45°. These lines will enable you to position and construct the plan view. Project the vertical lines of the end elevations down until they meet the 45° lines. From the point where they meet the line continue them

horizontally with the parallel motion or tee square. You can then project the vertical lines of the front elevation down and construct the plan.

Remember, all the work you do at this stage is construction work and should be drawn faintly with a 2H pencil. Once you are happy with your drawing, you can go over the main outlines with a softer, darker pencil such as an HB.

Orthographic drawings need to be clearly marked to show which type of projection has been used. There are standard symbols for this. They are shown in Figure 4.33. The symbols themselves are examples of orthographic drawing. They are front and end elevations of a truncated cone

shown in either first or third angle. The first angle symbol shows the end elevation projected to the right of the front elevation. The third angle symbol shows it in its true position to the left of the front elevation.

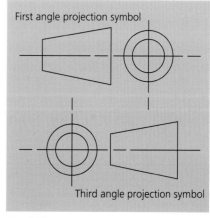

Fig. 4.33

THIRD ANGLE PROJECTION

Fig. 4.34

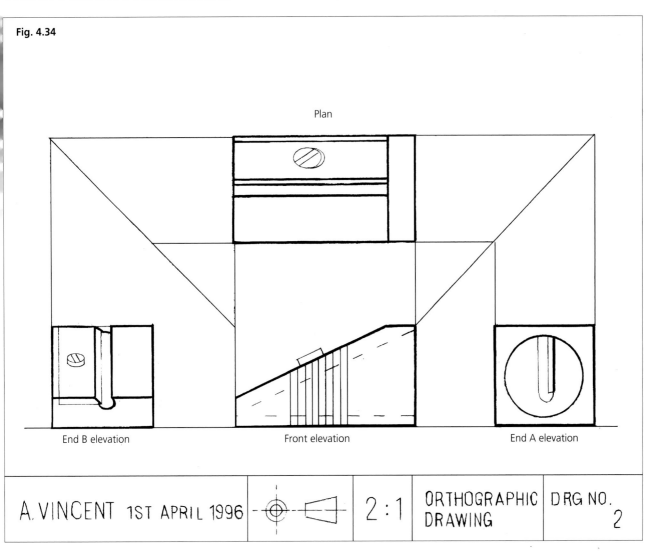

Plan

End B elevation   Front elevation   End A elevation

A. VINCENT 1ST APRIL 1996 | 2:1 | ORTHOGRAPHIC DRAWING | DRG NO. 2

The same pencil sharpener has been drawn in Figure 4.34. However, this time it has been drawn using third angle projection (you will see that the third angle symbol has been included in the title block). You will notice that, unlike first angle drawing, the plan view is positioned directly above the front elevation, and the end elevations are placed on the side nearest their true position. This makes third angle drawings easier to draw and much simpler to read and understand than first angle drawings. There is no need to worry about having to project the views through the object – they simply open out from the front elevation. The increasing popularity of third angle projection is probably due to its clarity – you can simply ask yourself, 'If I stand here, what will I see?'.

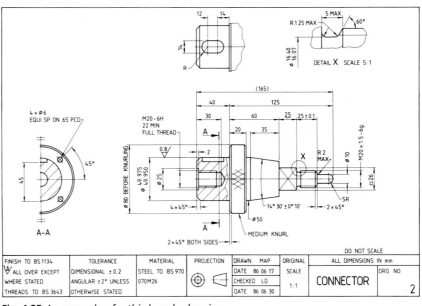

Fig. 4.35 *An example of a third angle drawing*

FINISH TO BS 1134	TOLERANCE	MATERIAL	PROJECTION	DRAWN MAP	ORIGINAL	ALL DIMENSIONS IN mm	
ALL OVER EXCEPT WHERE STATED THREADS TO BS 3643	DIMENSIONAL ± 0.2 ANGULAR ± 2° UNLESS OTHERWISE STATED	STEEL TO BS 970 070M26		DATE 86 06 17 CHECKED LD DATE 86 06 30	SCALE 1:1	CONNECTOR	DRG NO. 2

LINES

In technical drawing, different types of lines mean different things. The BSI documents show how they should be drawn.

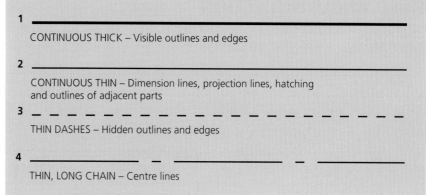

Fig. 4.36 *Some of the lines used in technical drawing*

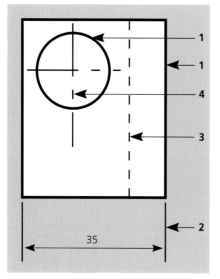

Fig. 4.37 *Uses of line*

Two thicknesses of line are used (thick lines should be twice the width of thin lines). It is normal practice to plan and draft drawings with thin 'construction' lines using a fairly hard pencil such as a 2H, and then go over the outline of objects with thick lines using a softer pencil such as an H or HB. The diagram in Figure 4.37 shows how the different types of line are used.

You can make technical drawings in either pencil or ink, but it is important not to mix the two. It is easier when working in ink to maintain the line thicknesses. Use a fine pen for the thin lines and a pen with a tip that is twice as wide for thick lines. All the lines in a drawing should be uniformly dense and bold.

DIMENSIONING

All working drawings, except assembly drawings, need to be dimensioned in order to show what size the object is in real life. The rules for dimensioning are clearly set out in both BSI booklets (BS308 and PP7308). Some of the main points are listed below.

1 Dimensions should be written on the drawing so that the measurements are the right way up when reading from the bottom or the from the right-hand side of the drawing.

2 Projection lines and dimension lines should be drawn outside the outline of the drawing whenever possible.

3 Smaller measurements should be written closer to the drawing.

4 Dimensions should be shown in millimetres. The symbol for millimetres (mm) does not have to be written on each dimension, as long as the drawing is clearly labelled to show that all dimensions are shown in millimetres.

5 The dimension should be written centrally above the dimension line.

6 Dimensions should not be repeated or used any more than necessary.

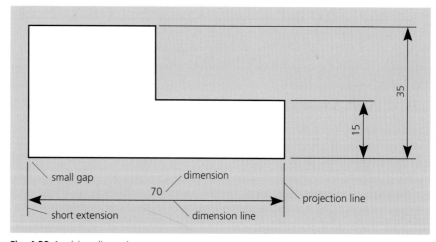

Fig. 4.38 *Applying dimensions*

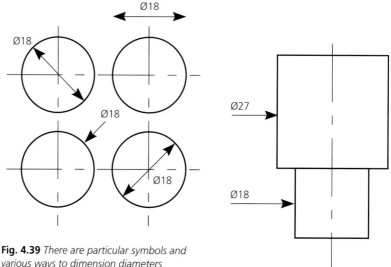

Fig. 4.39 *There are particular symbols and various ways to dimension diameters*

AUXILIARY VIEWS

Orthographic projections will be sufficient in most cases for you to show a complete picture of the object you are drawing. However, there may be times when you need to show parts that cannot be seen fully from the elevations in orthographic drawing, or you may want to show the object from a specific viewpoint. This can be done by drawing an extra view, known as an 'auxiliary view'. The drawing of the pencil sharpener, shown in Figure 4.40 does not show anything that cannot be seen in an orthographic projection, but an auxiliary view has been drawn to show what it would look like from an angle of 45° to the right. The drawing shows the pencil sharpener in three dimensions. The height of end A elevation is a true dimension (i.e. it is full size), but the length of the sharpener has been foreshortened because we are looking straight at it, and so is not a true dimension.

End A elevation

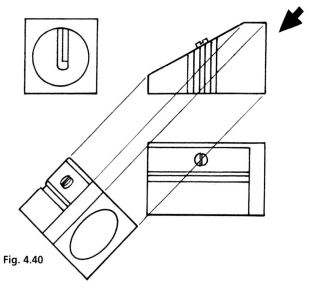

Fig. 4.40

True shape

Figure 4.41 includes an auxiliary view that has been drawn to show the true shape of a surface. This is useful in this case because it allows us to see the blade of the sharpener full size (rather than the foreshortened view in the normal plan). The length of the surface is projected by drawing it at right angles to the surface as shown on the front elevation, while the width is taken from the width of the end elevation.

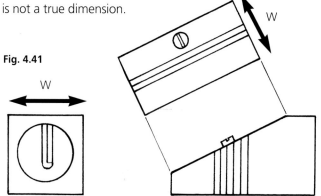

Fig. 4.41

Sections

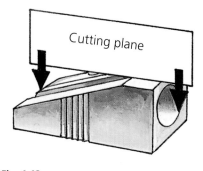

Fig. 4.42

There may be a time when you need to show the inside of an object and dashed lines would not allow you to show sufficient detail. In such a case you would need to draw a sectional view. Figure 4.42 shows the pencil sharpener about to be cut lengthwise by an imaginary cutting plane. The cut-off part of the sharpener nearest the viewer is 'discarded' and then the cross section of the remainder is drawn in detail. The parts of the object that are 'cut' are hatched with 45° lines, as shown in Figure 4.43.

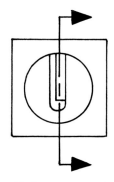

Fig. 4.43

The line with two arrows drawn on the end elevation in Figure 4.43 represents the cutting plane. The arrows show which part of the drawing is retained. Sectional views are often incorporated into orthographic drawings in order to make them clearer.

Figure 4.44 shows another sectional view through the pencil sharpener. In this case the line representing the cutting plane is drawn on the front elevation with the arrows indicating which part of the view is to be retained.

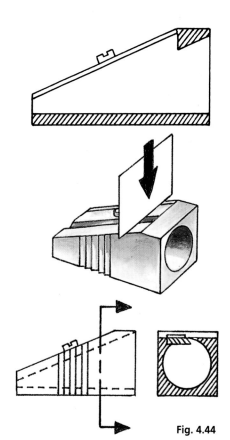

Fig. 4.44

Said Mooradun is a sales consultant at the Colindale branch of MFI, the UK's leading kitchen and bedroom retailer. MFI sells a wide range of units (manufactured by Hygena and Schreiber) which are supplied flat-packed, or as factory-assembled rigid units. MFI offer a comprehensive service, from planning to installing the chosen units for the consumer.

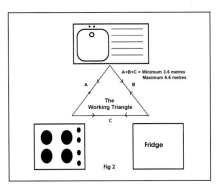

Planning a kitchen for a customer involves taking careful measurements of the room and noting the location of power points, the provision of plumbing and gas supply etc. to maximise the use of space. Said also has to take into account the 'working triangle' principle which recommends a minimum and maximum distance between the three main activity areas of a kitchen (the fridge, the sink and the hob). The working triangle is illustrated on the left.

ASSEMBLY DRAWINGS

Most of the things that you are likely to design and make will consist of more than one part. The individual components are usually shown on a parts drawing or a detail drawing, using orthographic projection. At some stage however, you will be required to show how the parts fit together to form the complete object. Drawings that show us how to do this are called 'assembly drawings'. The style of assembly drawings varies according to what you are designing and making. Sometimes a formal orthographic drawing of the assembled object is made, while on other occasions isometric, or perspective drawing might be used.

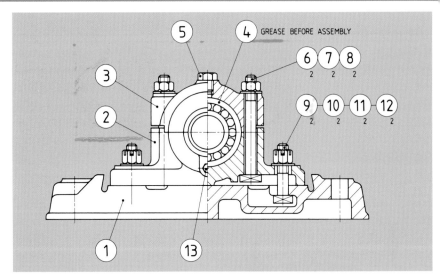

Fig. 4.45 *Example of a part-sectioned assembly drawing*

Sections

Sections or part sections are normally used in assembly drawings.

Figure 4.46 shows a sectional view of a car differential (final drive unit) used to show how the various parts are assembled.

Exploded drawings

Exploded drawing is another form of assembly drawing that is often used to show how component parts fit together and to give some idea of the sequence of assembly. Exploded drawings can be made using almost any 3-dimensional drawing method (isometric, perspective, etc.).

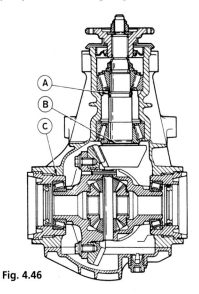

Fig. 4.46

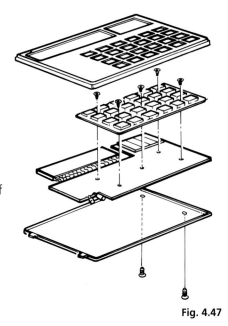

Fig. 4.47

*When planning a kitchen, Said often uses a magnetic planning board (like the one shown here) with moveable pieces representing the different units to be fitted, so that various layouts can be easily and quickly visualised. Alternatively, MFI can produce a floor plan and a 3D-**perspective drawing** of the new kitchen using computer-aided design.*

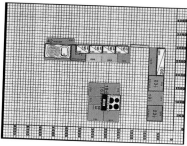

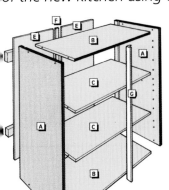

The illustration on the left shows an **exploded drawing** *from Hygena's assembly and installation guide, produced to enable customers to fit their own kitchen or bedroom units. Most Hygena and Schreiber kitchens have the FIRA (Furniture Industry Research Association) Gold Award for structural strength, workmanship and ease of assembly. Their well-designed assembly manuals contributed to their gaining the award – all you need to assemble and fit a Hygena or Schreiber kitchen is their installation guide, an Allen key, a couple of screwdrivers, a drill with a set of bits, a hammer, a saw, and a spirit level.*

The choice depends upon the information you want to convey. The drawing of the calculator in Figure 4.47 has been exploded vertically. Each part can be clearly seen, but some parts do overlap others. This has been done to create depth in the drawing and to show how each part relates to the other parts. Always take care to ensure that exploded drawings are made along a central axis where possible. The line of the imaginary path that connects the parts should be straight and level. This can be seen in the position of the screws which hold the calculator together in Figure 4.47.

You will probably come across exploded drawings if you buy any self-assembly models, toys or furniture. The manufacturers provide them to help the customer put the parts of a product together themselves. Car maintenance and repair manuals use assembly drawings to indicate the relative position of the parts and the order in which they are assembled or taken apart. Figure 4.48 shows a drawing of the components of a clutch pedal on a car and how they are assembled. Figure 4.49 shows part of the assembly instructions for a plastic model car kit.

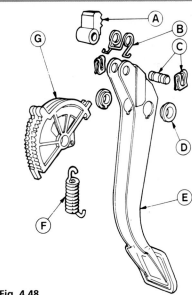

Fig. 4.48

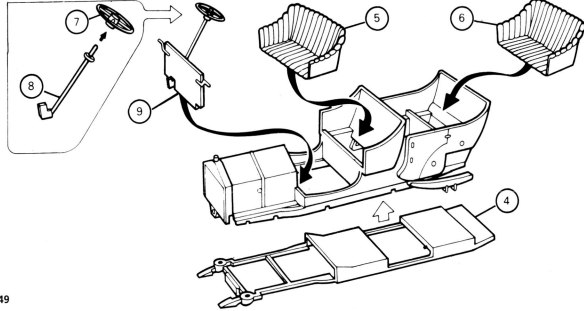

Fig. 4.49

Tony Childs and Eddie Arnold are designers at LINPAC, a company that designs and makes packaging. Almost every type of product – from cosmetics to horticultural produce – requires some form of packaging.

*The designers often use a basic **development** as a starting point, and then make adaptations according to customers' requirements. The photograph here shows a development on screen*

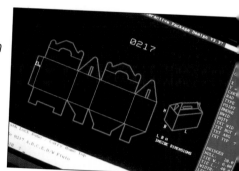

of a 'carry-home pack' for dot matrix printers. While working on a project, the designers ensure optimum 'palletisation' – in other words, they make sure that the design fits together well and the maximum number of packages will fit on to a pallet. The CAD package the designers use will also take into account the weight of the product and how high the

DEVELOPMENTS

A development is a drawing that shows an object as if all its surfaces had been opened out on to one plane. Developments are often used as patterns or templates when working in sheet materials because they show the true shape of the object. Figures 4.50 and 4.51 show a third angle orthographic drawing of a dice and its development. To understand it easily, imagine a cube made of card that has been unfolded. This unfolded shape is known as the development.

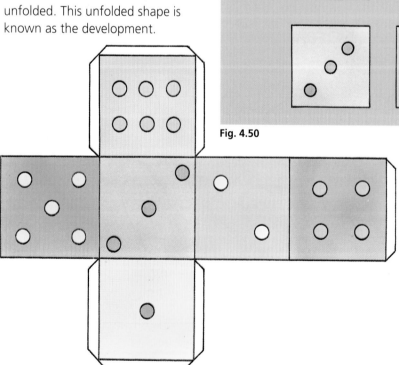

Fig. 4.50

Fig. 4.51 *The development of the cube with tabs*

Tabs can easily be added to developments so that they can be cut out and assembled. Developments are useful in model making and in packaging when simple box-like shapes are required.

It may be necessary to draw an auxiliary view of some objects in order to find the true shape before you can begin to make the development drawing. Auxiliary views are explained on page 69.

packages will be stacked in order to calculate the strength of the material needed.

LINPAC supplies all sorts of packaging. As well as cardboard boxes their range includes expanded polystyrene foam packs, paper sacks, plastic films, and metal closures and cans. They also design and provide customised artwork for printing. The photograph shown here includes some examples of the finished cardboard developments that LINPAC supply to their customers.

Developments of curved surfaces

Drawing developments of objects with curved surfaces requires the use of some simple geometry. To draw the development of a cylinder like the one shown in Figure 4.52 you need to draw an accurate front elevation and plan first. The height of the development will be the height of the front elevation. One way to find the width is to divide the plan into 12 equal 30° segments by measuring one and stepping off the rest with compasses or dividers. Now draw these segments as if they were flattened out – you will have drawn a rectangle, which is the true shape of the curved surface. Another way of finding the width of the development is to calculate mathematically the circumference of the plan.

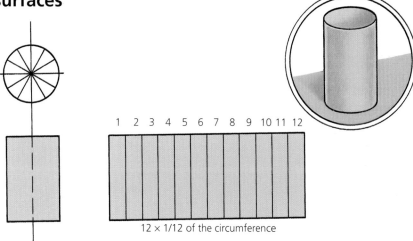

Fig. 4.52 *Stages in drawing the development of a cylinder*

The development of a cone is a sector of a circle (Fig. 4.53) and is drawn using the same principle. The true length of the cone's side (the slant height) provides the two straight edges of the development. To calculate how big a

sector the development needs to be, measure the distance across one 30° sector on the plan and step it off on the development 12 times.

The truncated cone in Figure 4.54 would be developed in a similar way, except that two concentric circles would have to be drawn. Try drawing a development of it yourself.

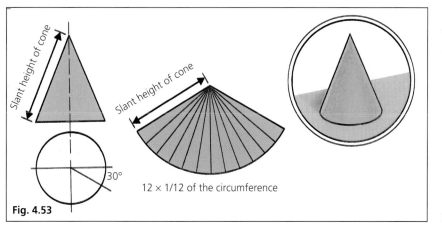

Fig. 4.53

Fig. 4.54

CONVENTIONS

Often there is not enough space on a drawing to write or draw everything in full. If this is the case, you can use standard conventions and abbreviations that have been developed by the BSI. Some of the more common abbreviations are listed in Figure 4.55. You can save a considerable amount of time if you use abbreviations. Check the BSI documents yourself for other abbreviations which may be useful.

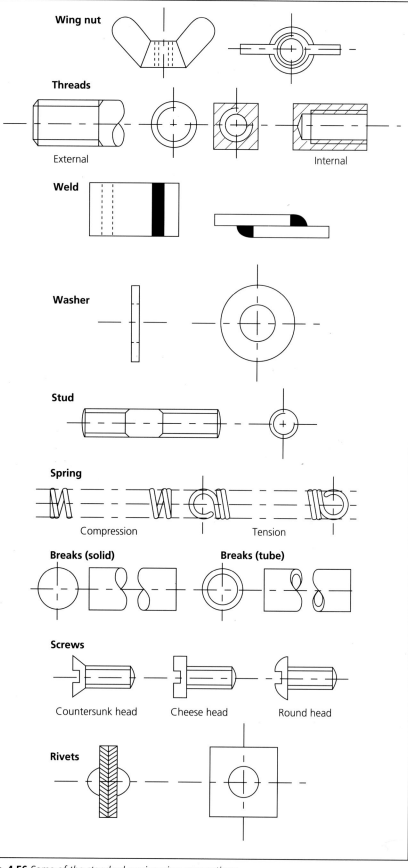

Fig. 4.56 *Some of the standard engineering conventions*

There are also standard graphic abbreviations, known as 'conventions'. A selection of these is shown in Figure 4.56. It would be very time consuming, for instance, to have to draw every thread on a bolt – it's far easier to draw its convention. Some computer software packages include these conventions in their clip art libraries.

Across flats (on head of nut or bolt)	AF
Centre line	C, CL or c
Computer-aided design	CAD
Computer-aided manufacture	CAM
Centimetre	cm
Centres	CRS
Counterbore	CBORE
Countersunk	CSK
Countersunk head	CSK HD
Diameter (before a dimension)	Ø
Diameter (in a note)	DIA
Drawing	DRG
External	EXT
Hexagon	HEX
Hexagonal head	HEX HD
Inside diameter	I/D
Internal	INT
Left hand	LH
Material	MATL
Metre	m
Millimetre	mm
Not to scale	NTS
Outside diameter	O/D
Radius (before a dimension)	R
Radius (in a note)	RAD
Right hand	RH

Fig. 4.55

74

Electronic symbols

When you draw designs for electronic circuits it would take you far too much time to draw every detail of each component. Like the standard conventions, there are symbols to represent the components in schematic diagrams that are drawn to show how the circuit is connected. Some of the more commonly used symbols are shown in Figure 4.57.

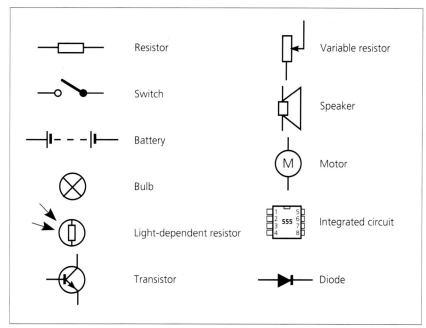

Fig. 4.57

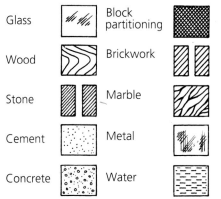

Fig. 4.58 *Conventions used to represent the range of materials used in the construction industry*

Architectural conventions

There is also a variety of conventions used to represent materials and features in architectural drawings (Figs 4.58 and 4.59). Most of the symbols and conventions used by architects are available in the form of dry transfers which are rubbed on to the drawing from a plastic backing sheet. They are also included in some computer software packages so that they can be used in computer-aided design.

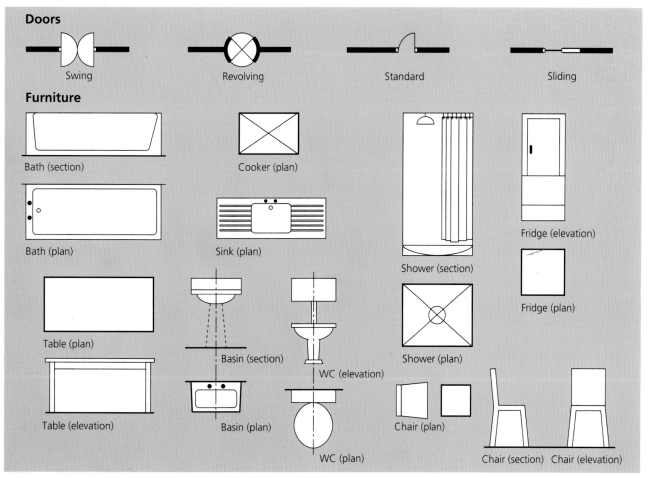

Fig. 4.59 *Some of the conventions used to identify features on architectural drawings*

Joanna Cholmeley is an architect at D B Lawrence & Associates in Sleaford. The practice was established 40 years ago by Mr Douglas Bernard Lawrence and specialised in the design of agricultural buildings. Nowadays, its designers are involved in a wide range of projects, including housing estates, school buildings and individually designed projects for specific clients.

At the start of a project, Joanna meets with the clients to discuss their requirements.

ARCHITECTURAL DRAWING

Architects make a number of drawings during the design and construction of a building. Preliminary drawings are used to visualise the brief they are given and communicate it to the client.

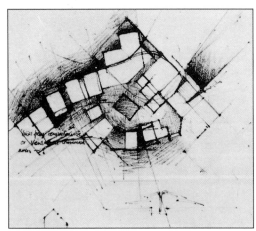

Fig. 4.60 *A preliminary architectural sketch made using pencil*

At this stage, drawings are often simple rough sketches which give a broad outline of the design without too much attention to constructional detail. They are usually drawn freehand in pencil, pen or marker depending upon the preferences of the person making the drawing.

Design drawings of a building need to be more detailed as they often have to be used by specialists such as structural engineers and surveyors. These drawings reflect the progress of the design – once any modifications are agreed, they are incorporated. Then production drawings are made.

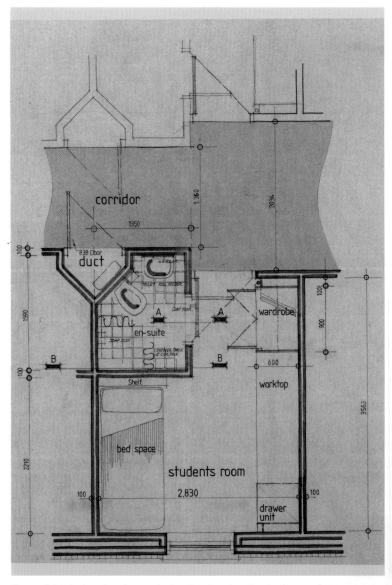

Figure 4.61 *A plan view from a design drawing showing the layout of a room*

After this, a feasibility study may be produced, and sketch plans are drawn to show alternative elevations before the scheme is approved by the client. The sketch view on the left was prepared for a 3-storey teaching block at the King's School in Grantham.

Then, detailed **design drawings** *and* **production drawings** *are prepared which include enough detail to satisfy building regulations and gain planning approval, and for tenders to be obtained. The drawing on this page shows details of part of a laboratory extension to King's School.*

Once a satisfactory tender has been accepted, work begins on site. Joanna closely supervises the work to ensure that it is carried out in accordance with the **working drawings** *and that it is on schedule.*

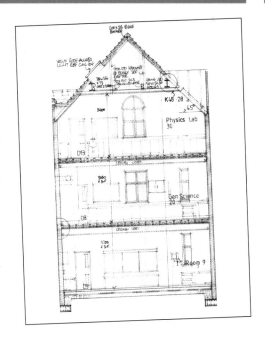

Production drawings include working drawings which show the various elevations and the plan views (Fig. 4.61) together with precise technical information regarding the construction of the building. These drawings are not only used to convey information to the builder, but also to apply for planning permission and building regulations approval from the local authority. Production drawings have to include all the information that is needed to work out exactly what is required in terms of materials, to make costings, obtain quotations for the work to be carried out, and finally, to instruct contractors.

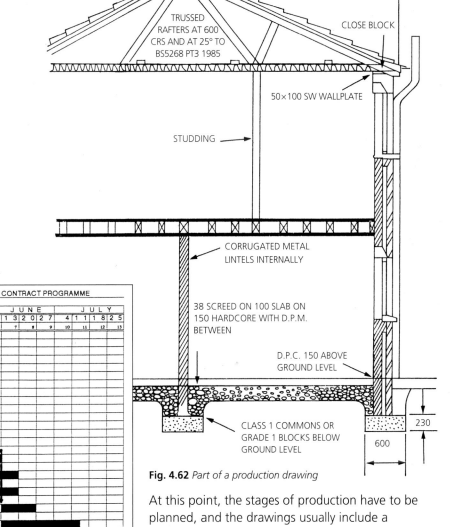

RIDGE TILE BEDDED IN MORTAR

TRUSSED RAFTERS AT 600 CRS AND AT 25° TO BS5268 PT3 1985

CLOSE BLOCK

50×100 SW WALLPLATE

STUDDING

CORRUGATED METAL LINTELS INTERNALLY

38 SCREED ON 100 SLAB ON 150 HARDCORE WITH D.P.M. BETWEEN

D.P.C. 150 ABOVE GROUND LEVEL

CLASS 1 COMMONS OR GRADE 1 BLOCKS BELOW GROUND LEVEL

230

600

Fig. 4.62 *Part of a production drawing*

At this point, the stages of production have to be planned, and the drawings usually include a construction programme or work schedule. This sets out the order in which the work is to be carried out and allocates a time for each individual task.

CONTRACT PROGRAMME													
Year		1 9 9 4											
Month		M A Y				J U N E				J U L Y			
Week Com	2	9	1 6	2 3	3 0	6	1 3	2 0	2 7	4	1 1	1 8	2 5
Week No	1	2	3	4	5	6	7	8	9	10	11	12	13
OPERATIONS													
Set up Site													
Site Strip													
Set Out													
Excavate Foundations													
Concrete Foundations													
Erect Steelwork													
Brickwork Substructure													
Hardcore slab													
Concrete slab													
Truss Tray Lining													
Brickwork Superstructure													
Tile Roof													

Fig. 4.63 *Part of a work schedule*

Putting it into practice

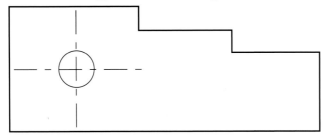

1 Copy the drawing shown above and then dimension it according to BSI standards.

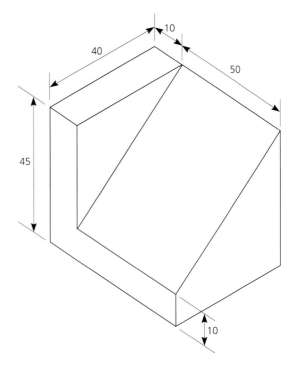

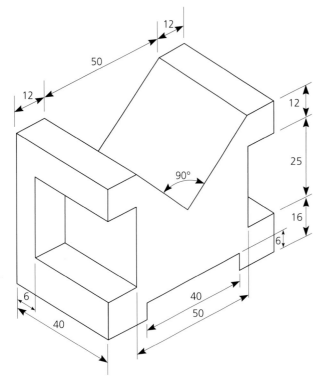

2 The drawing above shows an engineering tool called a vee block. Draw the vee block accurately using first angle orthographic projection.

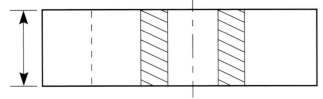

3 The drawing shown above consists of several different types of line. Identify each type and explain their uses.

4 Make a third angle orthographic drawing of the wedge block shown in the drawing above and then draw an auxiliary view to show the true shape of the sloping surface.

5 Choose a simple object such as a matchbox, cassette or CD case and make a section drawing of it.

6 Make an exploded drawing of a ballpen.

7 Develop a simple package to hold a pencil rubber or a pencil sharpener.

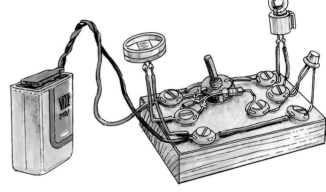

8 Look at the electrical circuit shown above and then draw it as a circuit diagram.

9 What do the following abbreviations stand for?

a) CL	d) CRS	g) HEX HD
b) cm	e) DIA	h) I/D
c) A/F	f) DRG	i) MATL

10 Make a simple architectural plan view of a room in your house.

5·Real-World Design

CORPORATE IMAGE DESIGN

English Rose Company

The photograph above shows a package designed to hold a rose plant. It was designed as part of a corporate image used to promote the English Rose Company.

The company, under a different name, was founded in 1978, growing in that year a relatively small crop of 10,000 roses. Now, over a million roses are grown each year, making it one of the largest rose growers in the country. The business supplies plants to supermarkets and garden centres nationwide, and exports to Holland and the USA.

When the company started to sell direct to the public, it decided to launch a subsidiary of the firm, with a distinctive brand image.

This decision created the need for a cohesive corporate identity, which would project the image of the new company in its advertising, package design, vehicle livery and business stationery.

The aim of creating a recognisable corporate image was to increase the company's share of the market by improving the way in which both the company and its products were presented to the public.

On pages 80–83 you can see how the English Rose Company's corporate image was developed.

ENVIRONMENTAL DESIGN

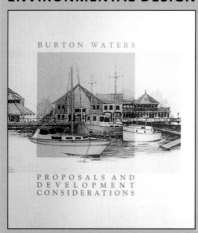

Burton Waters

Burton Waters is a major environmental design project that involves changing the use of 137 acres of riverside land to create a marina, lakes and parkland, along with associated facilities such as parking, restaurants and shops. It is, therefore, a large and very expensive project – and it is being financed by a number of business people and organisations.

Not surprisingly, local people and groups who have a particular concern for environmental issues wanted to be assured that the project would be an improvement to the area and that it would not harm the existing natural environment.

The architectural design company Costall Allen Design were commissioned to both design the development and to present the environmental case for it. To communicate the details of the design, it produced a very detailed report and environmental statement, and a scale model of the complete project.

Pages 84–87 show details from the report and the scale model.

CORPORATE CLOTHING DESIGN

le Shuttle

The garments in the photo above are the result of an Anglo–French design collaboration. They have been manufactured by the Wensum Corporate Company as part of a complete corporate clothing package for 'le Shuttle', the Eurotunnel train service that runs through the Channel Tunnel.

Corporate clothing design is rather different to design for high fashion. There are many considerations that have to be taken into account to create clothes for all the employees of a company. For 'le Shuttle', garments had to be designed for all types of jobs – from ticket collectors to train drivers and loading staff. Consequently there were many technical factors to take into account. For instance, the fabric for the loading staff needed to be strong enough and the design allow enough movement for the bending and stretching they would need to do. Also, the designs had to be suitable for the whole size range of the employees (a typical corporate women's size range runs from size 8 to size 24).

The designs shown on pages 88–91 are those for the customer contact staff (such as ticket collectors).

English Rose Company

The illustrations shown here are taken from the graphic designer's sketches and drawings for this project.

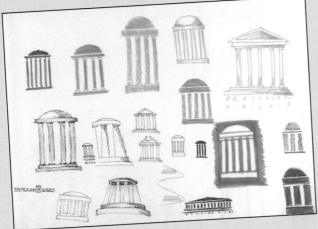

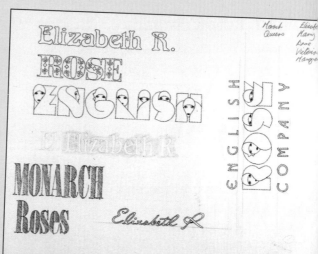

Company name

The designer's first task was to suggest suitable names for the subsidiary company. The English nature of the rose was taken as a theme and various possibilities were explored before deciding on 'The English Rose Company'.

The sketches shown above and on the right illustrate some of the initial ideas for getting across a feeling of 'Englishness'. They have been very quickly drawn using marker and fine line pens.

Logo design

Once a company name had been established, the next task was to design a logo. The inspiration for this came from a traditional playing card design. The sketches below show how the idea for the company logo was developed from this starting point. The idea for a crown above the logo came from English hallmarks. These are the marks which are stamped on to silver and gold to indicate the purity of the metal, the makers of the object, and the year it was made.

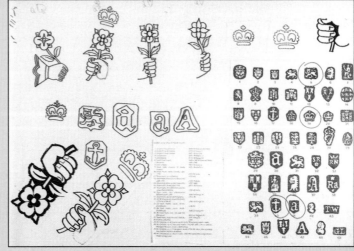

Developing ideas

The sketches on this page show how the designer developed the original idea and the hallmark theme into a suitable design which has an 'English' feel to it.

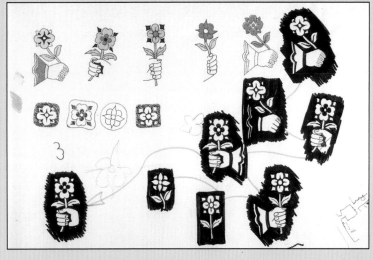

Marker pen has been used to highlight the ideas. This makes the ideas stand out and also creates a more realistic 'hallmarked' image.

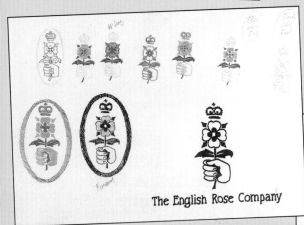

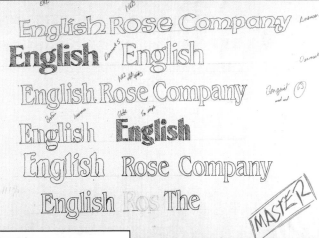

The drawings on the right show how the designer has experimented with typefaces and lettering. Again, the aim here was to maintain the traditional 'English' theme.

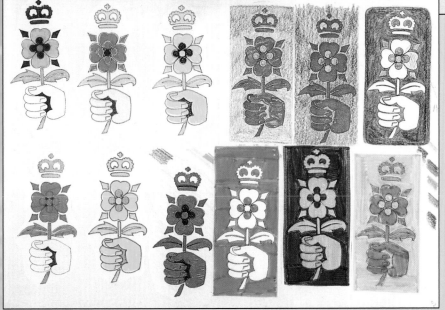

The illustration on the left shows how the designer considered colour coordination. Coloured pencil and marker pen has been used to explore possible colour combinations. Along the edge, you can see where the designer has begun to match them to Pantone colours.

These illustrations show how the designer arrived at the final logo design. Notice that the rectangular 'hallmark' background of the logo has been changed in favour of a softer, more classic elliptical design. The name of the company has also been shortened, to 'English Rose Company'.

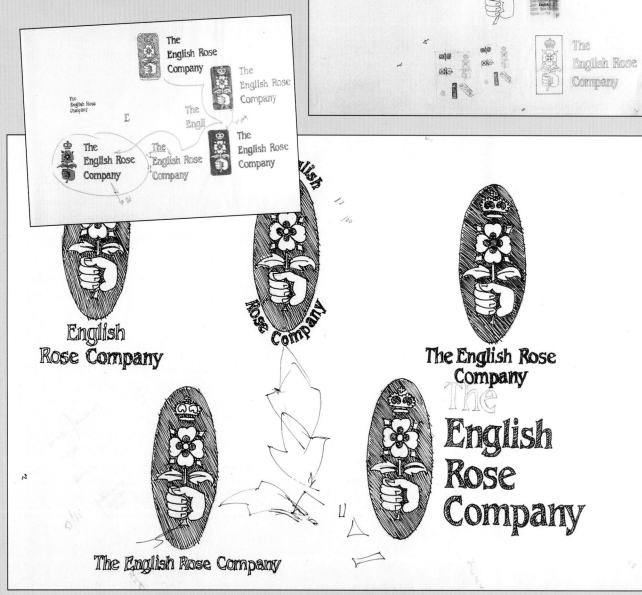

The final artwork for the logo is shown on the left. This will be photographed so that a printing plate can be made from it. Notice the registration marks on the artwork.
These will be used by the printer to accurately align the work when printing. They are very important when printing in more than one colour so that each colour fits together perfectly.

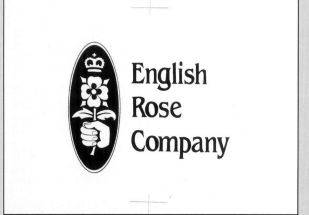

The photographs on this page show the final designs which were presented to the client. Above are the vehicle livery, business card and headed paper designs. They have been finished off by mounting on to foam board and then carefully trimming to shape. On the right is the full-size development for the rose plant package. It is folded to create a six-sided container as shown by the scale model in the photograph.

BURTON WATERS

The Report and Environmental Statement

The logo used for this project was designed to show human leisure pursuits, represented by sailing, in harmony with the natural habitat, represented by birds and fish. It is shown below in detail, and can be seen on each page of the report. Other interesting design features of the report to note include the use of a water image, rectangular shaped shades of subtle colours and simple line drawings.

Below, you can see a typical page from the report. It shows some interesting aspects of layout. White space has been used to good effect, and the text is in a two-column format which makes it easier to read. The line drawings of the boats and quayside show the designers' ideas of what part of the finished development might look like. The drawings were made using a pencil, and the colour shades were added during the printing process. The pages are numbered, and each displays both the project logo and the designers' logo.

PLANNING AGREEMENTS

2.43 The applicant company will be willing to enter into Agreements with West Lindsey District Council under Section 106 of the Town and Country Planning Act 1990, to ensure that the site development and management is in accordance with agreed principles. The District Council will probably wish to programme, by such an agreement, the commencement and completion of particular works and places of development within the site. For example, it could be seen as reasonable to ensure that the Marina basins and other lakes are excavated and available for use before the dwellings and commercial elements are occupied or brought into use. As the site is divided into two sections, it is suggested that the Marina basins and their associated development, is subject to one agreement. Another separate agreement may then relate to the water sports, fishing lakes and associated commercial developments. The applicant company will comply with all reasonable requirements of the Council to safeguard and ensure that the development is properly carried out and proceeds in a controlled manner.

SITE MANAGEMENT

2.44 Whilst the applicant company will be responsible for the overall management of the development site, and the co-ordination and maintenance of the highest possible standards, additional management schemes will be established to give more direct and effective control over the operation of specific uses and activities. It is envisaged for example that a management scheme, involving freehold or leasehold property owners, will operate the marina and be responsible for its running and maintenance.

2.45 Effective management and security is essential for a complex of this character and diversity, and the applicant company will undertake, through agreements, to ensure that the executive control is positively and properly exercised.

2.46 It can therefore be seen that the development of the site in the manner shown on the plans accompanying the outline application lodged with the District Council and as described in Section 2 of this report, can be achieved without detriment to any elements of infrastructure in the area.

14

Costall Allen Design

It is useful to look at documents of this type to learn about style. This report is an A3-size folder with a card front and back, and a ring-type binder similar to that used on many Design & Technology projects. Could some aspects of this style be used to improve the presentation of your project folders?

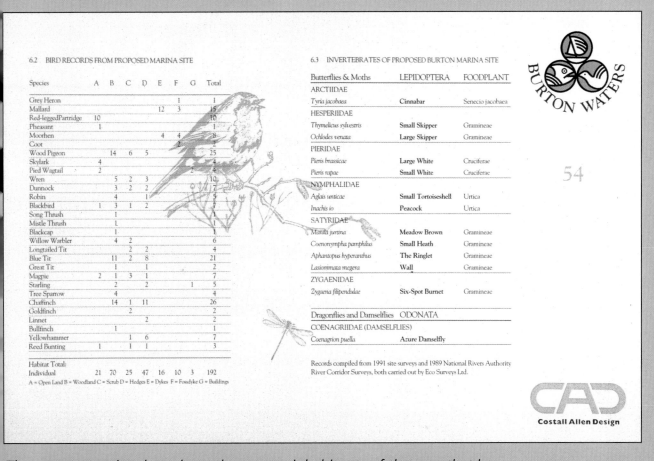

6.2 BIRD RECORDS FROM PROPOSED MARINA SITE

Species	A	B	C	D	E	F	G	Total
Grey Heron					1			1
Mallard			12	3				15
Red-legged Partridge	10							10
Pheasant	1							1
Moorhen				4	4			8
Coot				2				2
Wood Pigeon		14	6	5				25
Skylark	4							4
Pied Wagtail	2				2			4
Wren		5	2	3				10
Dunnock		3	2	2				
Robin		4	1					5
Blackbird	1	3	1	2				7
Song Thrush		1						1
Mistle Thrush		1						1
Blackcap		1						1
Willow Warbler		4	2					6
Longtailed Tit			2	2				4
Blue Tit		11	2	8				21
Great Tit		1		1				2
Magpie	2	1	3	1				7
Starling		2		2		1		5
Tree Sparrow		4						4
Chaffinch		14	1	11				26
Goldfinch			2					2
Linnet				2				2
Bullfinch		1						1
Yellowhammer			1	6				7
Reed Bunting	1		1	1				3

Habitat Total:
Individual   21   70   25   47   16   10   3   192

A = Open Land B = Woodland C = Scrub D = Hedges E = Dykes F = Fossdyke G = Buildings

6.3 INVERTEBRATES OF PROPOSED BURTON MARINA SITE

Butterflies & Moths	LEPIDOPTERA	FOODPLANT
ARCTIIDAE		
Tyria jacobaea	Cinnabar	Senecio jacobaea
HESPERIIDAE		
Thymelicus sylvestris	Small Skipper	Gramineae
Ochlodes venata	Large Skipper	Gramineae
PIERIDAE		
Pieris brassicae	Large White	Cruciferae
Pieris rapae	Small White	Cruciferae
NYMPHALIDAE		
Aglais urticae	Small Tortoiseshell	Urtica
Inachis io	Peacock	Urtica
SATYRIDAE		
Manila jurtina	Meadow Brown	Gramineae
Coenonympha pamphilus	Small Heath	Gramineae
Aphantopus hyperanthus	The Ringlet	Gramineae
Lasiommata megera	Wall	Gramineae
ZYGAENIDAE		
Zygaena filipendulae	Six-Spot Burnet	Gramineae

Dragonflies and Damselflies	ODONATA	
COENAGRIIDAE (DAMSELFLIES)		
Coenagrion puella	Azure Damselfly	

Records compiled from 1991 site surveys and 1989 National Rivers Authority River Corridor Surveys, both carried out by Eco Surveys Ltd.

BURTON WATERS

54

Costall Allen Design

The report contains data about the current inhabitants of the area that has been collected over a period of time. Such research is necessary to ensure that the development does not upset the balance of nature, and that the correct type of natural habitat is preserved. It is often difficult to present tables of data in an interesting format. Here, in an effort to enhance the presentation, the designers have used another line drawing, this time set behind the text.

This is a page that has been made up from a portion of an Ordnance Survey map. Details have been added to show the location of the development. The right-hand portion has been 'faded out' so that the logos and page number can be inserted to retain the overall style of the report. When parts of maps are copied, the publishers of the document have to get permission from the copyright owners, in this case, HMSO (Her Majesty's Stationery Office).

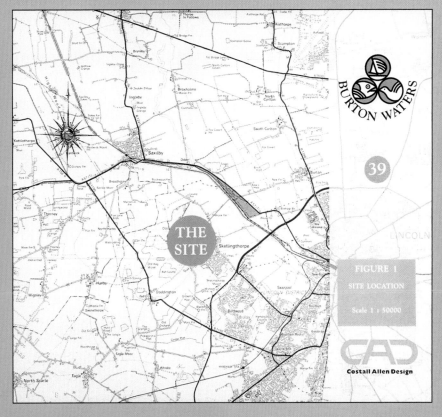

Maps and models

The map on the right is another location map. This one has been simplified in order to pick out only the detail that the designers want to draw attention to. It shows where the development will be located in relation to the nearest town, nearby villages, major roads, the Fossdyke Navigation (the Fossdyke is a canal built by the Romans to link the rivers Witham and Trent) and the railway line.

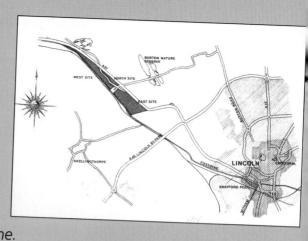

The map below is the designers' plan of the site. Notice how it has been sensitively coloured using pencil crayons over a textured surface (see page 37). Also, colour has been added to the line drawings. Such drawings of completed projects are often referred to as 'artist's impressions'. They are made to make the completed development look its best, in this case with boats and attractive buildings.

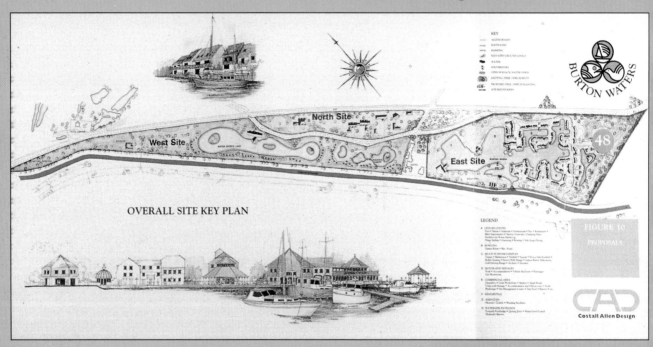

OVERALL SITE KEY PLAN

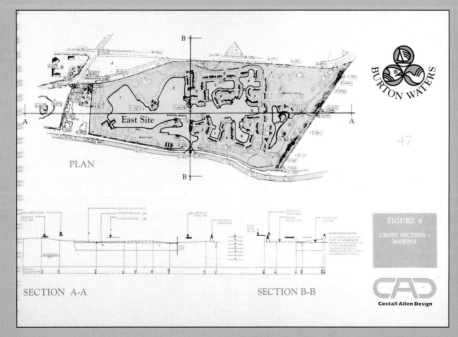

The map on the left shows two sectional views through the actual marina part of the development. They indicate the depth of the water and the access to the marina for boats from the Fossdyke Navigation. The sectional views also show the flood defences.

SECTION A-A   SECTION B-B

The main means of communicating the design for Burton Waters was through the medium of a scale model. The model was produced to a scale of 1:1000, and even then it is 2.9 metres long! In the photograph on the left you can see members of the design team discussing aspects of the project.

The model has been made from a whole range of modelling media, including wood, paper, card, plastic sheet and plaster of Paris (see modelling materials on pages 52–54). If you look very carefully at the close-up photographs of the model shown here, you will see a small error – the masts of the sail boats are too long to fit under the footbridges. Even professional model makers sometimes make mistakes!

The model for Burton Waters turned out to be so impressive that it now stands on display in the entrance foyer of the developer's offices.

le Shuttle

The brief

On the left you can see part of the brief that the Wensum Corporate Company, the manufacturers of the 'le Shuttle' uniforms, were given to work from – the Eurotunnel logo, a sample of fabric covering the train seats and the corporate Pantone colours.

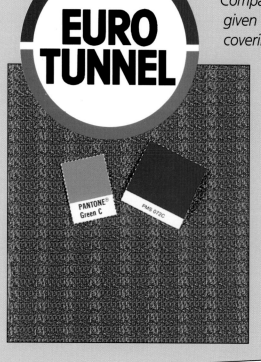

Initial concepts were sketched in colour, using coloured pencils and marker pens that use the Pantone colour reference system. The sketches shown here are the designers' initial ideas for women's trousers and jacket, and a men's jacket, with fabric samples attached to them.

Making prototypes

Once the designers were happy with their ideas, prototypes were made up so that they could be shown at a presentation in Paris, where Wensum were competing with others for the contract to design all the uniforms for Eurotunnel. The photograph on the left shows the garments that were made up for the presentation being modelled by professional models. Together with the designers, Pierre Balmain, Wensum won the competition.

A change in the brief

After the presentation, the design brief changed. This was because a name, 'le Shuttle', had been created for the train service, and a logo had been designed for it. You can see the logo below.

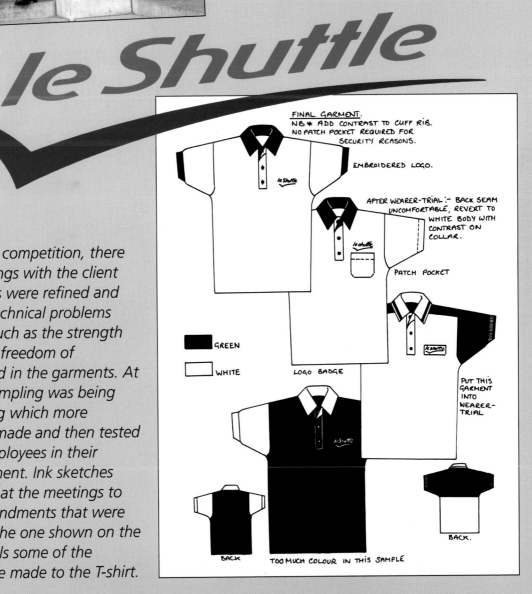

After winning the competition, there were many meetings with the client where the designs were refined and developed, and technical problems were discussed, such as the strength of fabric, and the freedom of movement needed in the garments. At the same time, sampling was being carried out, during which more prototypes were made and then tested by 'le Shuttle' employees in their working environment. Ink sketches were often made at the meetings to illustrate any amendments that were to be made, like the one shown on the right, which details some of the changes that were made to the T-shirt.

Developing designs

Other design developments included the rejection of a women's zipped jacket (the initial colour sketch for this is shown on the left), on the grounds that, following a wearer-trial, it was found to look untidy if it was left undone, and would therefore always have to be kept zipped up which would be uncomfortable for employees indoors and in hot weather. The design of the tie was also changed, to reflect the new logo. Below, you can see the original sketch for the tie, with stripes in the corporate colours, along with a mock-up of the new design, which uses repeated images of the new logo to create a pattern.

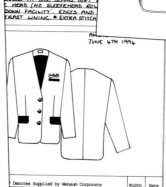

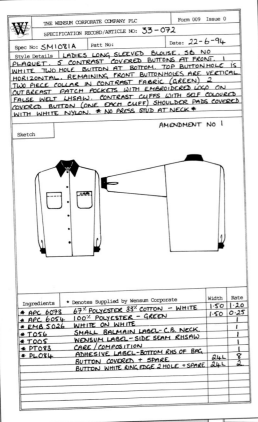

	THE WENSUM CORPORATE COMPANY PLC		Form 009 Issue 0
	SPECIFICATION RECORD/ARTICLE No: **33 - 072**		

Spec No: **SM1081A**   Patt No: Date: **22-6-94**

Style Details | LADIES LONG SLEEVED BLOUSE. SB NO PLAQUET. 5 CONTRAST COVERED BUTTONS AT FRONT. 1 WHITE TWO HOLE BUTTON AT BOTTOM. TOP BUTTONHOLE IS HORIZONTAL. REMAINING FRONT BUTTONHOLES ARE VERTICAL. TWO PIECE COLLAR IN CONTRAST FABRIC (GREEN) 2 OUTBREAST PATCH POCKETS WITH EMBROIDERED LOGO ON FALSE WELT LHSAW. CONTRAST CUFFS WITH SELF COLOURED COVERED BUTTON (ONE EACH CUFF) SHOULDER PADS COVERED WITH WHITE NYLON. * NO PRESS STUD AT NECK *

AMENDMENT No 1

Sketch

Ingredients	* Denotes Supplied by Wensum Corporate	Width	Rate
* APC 6073	67% POLYESTER 33% COTTON - WHITE	1·50	1·20
* APC 6054	100% POLYESTER - GREEN	1·50	0·25
* EMB 5026	WHITE ON WHITE		1
* TO56	SMALL BALMAIN LABEL- C.B. NECK		1
* TOO5	WENSUM LABEL- SIDE SEAM RHSAW		1
* PTO83	CARE / COMPOSITION		1
* PLO84	ADHESIVE LABEL- BOTTOM RHS OF BAG		1
	BUTTON COVERED + SPARE	24L	8
	BUTTON WHITE RING EDGE 2 HOLE + SPARE	24L	2

THE WENSUM CORPORATE COMPANY PLC

SPECIFICATION RECORD/ARTICLE No: **31 - 01**

1077A   Patt No: **SM1077**

SB BUTTON 3 LADIES JACKET 1 OUTBREAST CONTRAST JETTE EMBROIDERED ABOVE. 2 OUTS AP POCKETS. CENTRE BACK SE ENERS AT SIDE SEAMS. SOFT HEAD (NO SLEEVEHEAD ROL DOWN FACILITY'. EDGES AND RAST LINING. * EXTRA STITCH

JUNE 4TH 1994

Denotes Supplied by Wensum Corporate	Width	Rate
EMERALD 55% POLYESTER 45% WOOL	1·50	1·50
ROYAL 55% POLYESTER 45% WOOL	1·50	0·12
ROYAL LINING 100% POLYESTER	1·50	1·02
LE SHUTTLE" EMBROIDERY WHITE		
LE SHUTTLE" LOGO BUTTONS AND SPARE	48L	4
WENSUM/NAME LOOPFOLD LHSAW ABOVE SIDE		1
LABEL/COMP/SIZE UNDER WENSUM NAME LABEL		1
BALMAIN LARGE. BACK NECK FACING		1
MINI SIZE MARKER		1
MINI FITTING MARKER		1

The final specifications

Each time a change was made to a design, a new style sheet was written up. The style sheets on this page show the final specifications for a women's jacket and blouse. As you can see, there are lots of written details on the sheets, as well as ink drawings of the garment.

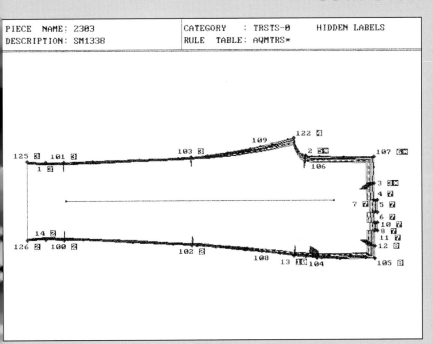

```
PIECE  NAME: 2303          CATEGORY   : TRSTS-0     HIDDEN LABELS
DESCRIPTION: SM1338        RULE  TABLE: AQMTRS*
```

Once the final specifications were drawn up, a pattern master was drawn, and a pattern grade created, from which the garments were cut and made. (A pattern grade includes all the enlargements or reductions for all the sizes that are to be made.) The grade shown here is for part of the women's trouser pattern, and was produced using CAD.

The photographs on this page show 'le Shuttle' staff modelling the final designs for the customer contact staff uniforms.

Acknowledgements

The publishers would like to thank the following:

For their help in providing case study material:

Christine Laver at Griffen Paper Mill; John Storrs at Berol Ltd; John Greed; Ken Allen and Sue Forbes at Costall Allen Design; Colin Plant; Martin and Mel Holliday at Chiselwood; Maureen and Bill Atkinson at Alona Designs; Alan Miller Bunford; Tom Murray at European Gas Turbines Ltd; Hygena/MFI; Mick Thornton at LINPAC; Jo Cholmeley and Robin Blackbourn at D.B. Lawrence Associates; Jean Phillips and Sue McCombe at The Wensum Corporate Company.

For their help with location photography:

Northwood School, Hillingdon (Head of Technology: Jon Lambert; Pupil: Natalie Matharu)

William Farr C of E Comprehensive School, Welton (Head of Technology: Mike Finney)

For their help with supplying materials for photographing:

EMA Model Supplies and Daler Rowney

For permission to reproduce photographs and illustrations:

Airfix (Fig. 4.49); Autodesk Ltd (Fig. 4.15); Berol Ltd (Figs 2.23 right, 2.25 top, 2.29, 2.33 top); Blundell Harling Limited (Figs 4.6, 4.7); BSI (Figs 4.29, 4.35, 4.45); Butterworth Architecture (Fig. 4.60); Rebecca Capper, Spalding Girls' High School (Fig. 2.35); Colin Chapman (Fig. 2.36); Costall Allen Design (Figs 4.61, 4.63); Daily Telegraph (Fig. 1.28); Daler Rowney (Fig. 3.14 left, 3.41); EMA Model Supplies (Figs 3.36, 3.37, 3.42); Mike Finney (Fig. 2.32); Friskair (Fig. 3.16); Haynes Publishers (Figs 4.46, 4.48); Imagelink (p.5, top); Julia Kendall (Figs 1.10, 3.3, 3.24, 3.25, 3.26, 3.27); Letraset UK Ltd (Fig. 2.51); Liberty (Fig. 2.17); Tom Morgan, De Aston School, Market Rasen (Figs. 2.3, 2.25 bottom, 2.30, 2.31, 2.33 bottom, 2.34, 3.1, page 55 right); Colin Plant (Figs. 2.2, 2.29); Roland Digital Group (Figs. 4.20, 4.21); Rotring UK (Figs 4.5, 4.11); Casey Rutland, Northwood School, Hillingdon (Fig. 2.40); Science Photo Library (p. 5 middle left, Figs 2.1, 3.38, p. 60 top); Simair (Fig. 3.12); Sittingbourne paper company Ltd (p.7, top); TAG Developments Ltd (Fig. 4.18); Techsoft UK Ltd (Fig. 4.14); Walton Designs (Fig. 4.2); Wensum Corporate Company (Figs. 3.19, 3.20); Zefa (Figs 2.12, 3.34, page 58 top)

Index

Index